D1302106

THOROUGHBRED

# THE ONTARIO

# PUBLIC SCHOOL HYGIENE

BY

## A. P. KNIGHT, M.A., M.D.

PROFESSOR OF PHYSIOLOGY

*Queen's University, Kingston*

**Authorized by the Minister of Education for Ontario**

FOR USE IN

**Forms IV and V of the Public Schools**

TORONTO

THE COPP, CLARK COMPANY, LIMITED

# PREFACE

The present volume summarizes very briefly the teaching of the Reader in hygiene used in Ontario Public Schools, and contains much additional matter, especially in regard to hygiene. All boys and girls before they reach forms IV and V acquire some knowledge of animal physiology without any formal instruction, and they may be led to acquire a much fuller knowledge with a little assistance from the teacher. A detailed knowledge, however, such as is included in many school physiologies, is a mistake. Anatomical dissections and physiological demonstrations are not suitable for school children.

For school children the important matter is hygiene—a knowledge of the laws of health. If, during their school days, children learn how to care for their health, and acquire health habits as they certainly should, they are laying the best possible foundation for doing their daily work with real enjoyment, and for bearing the stress and strain of adult life without danger of a physical or mental break-down.

Those physicians and teachers who read the proofs of the Reader in hygiene have been kind enough to read the proofs of this book. In addition, R. Ramsay Wright, M.A., LL.D., Vice-President of the University of Toronto, and C. K. Clarke, M.D., LL.D., Dean of the Faculty of Medicine in the University of Toronto, have read the proofs of the *Nervous System*, *Special Senses*, and *Family Stock*. A. McPhedran, M.B., Professor of Medicine in the University of Toronto, and Dr. Helen MacMurchy, Toronto, have read all the proofs.

Apart from my personal experience and observations, the chief sources from which I have drawn material have been the standard physiologies of Howell, Ott, Schäffer, Stewart, Hall, and Foster.

On special topics I have made use of original monographs or reports. I am especially indebted to Professor C. F. Hodge on *The Physiological Aspects of the Liquor Problem;* Sir Victor Horsley and Dr. Sturge's *Alcohol and the Human Body;* Sedgwick's *Principles of Sanitary Science and Public Health;* R. McKenzie Moore's *Comparative Mortality Among Assured Lives of Abstainers and Non-abstainers;* J. W. Seaver's *Effects of Nicotine; Reports* of the Ontario, Massachusetts, and Pennsylvania's State Boards of Health; *Milk and its Relation to the Public Health,* being Bulletin 41 of the Public Health and Marine Hospital Service, Washington, D.C., 1908; Dr. A. C. Abbott's *Hygiene of Transmissible Disease; The Life of Pasteur,* by René Vallery-Radot; *Floating Matter of the Air,* by Professor Tyndall; *Personal Hygiene,* by Dr. W. L. Pyle; *The Jukes,* by R. L. Dugdale; the *Jukes-Edwards,* by A. E. Winship; and above all, the notable papers read at the International Congress of School Hygiene, in London, in 1907.

The illustrations in the chapters on *Milk* are reproduced from Bulletin 41 of the Public Health and Marine Hospital Service, Washington, D.C., with the kind permission of the Acting Surgeon-General.

A. P. K.

# TABLE OF CONTENTS

# THE
# PUBLIC SCHOOL HYGIENE

## CHAPTER I

### WHY WE STUDY HYGIENE

Before you enter upon the study of hygiene let me point out some reasons why you should do so.

Young people should study hygiene, or the laws of health, not merely for their own health's sake but in order to be able to save life. The very essence of Christianity consists in working for the good of others. John Howard, the jail reformer, and Louis Pasteur, the French scientist, are outstanding examples of men who spent their lives in striving to benefit mankind.

But you do not need to be great men in order to be of service to others. Your services are needed in enforcing health laws and regulations in the case of innumerable cellars, streets, yards, school-houses, and churches throughout Canada. You should consider yourselves specially responsible for the cleanliness of at least one yard and one cellar—your own.

If you live in the country you may see scores of wells, barn-yards, cow-stables, and backyards so neglected and filthy that they are a nuisance and a menace to human life. These evils it will be your duty, when you become men and women, to remedy as far as you can.

If you live in a city or town, and see dirty milkshops, sunless tenements, impure water-supply, and the sickness and death that result from these, your knowledge of hygiene should speedily prompt you to do what you can toward putting an end to these evils. More or less of this work you ought to do, as soon as you have learned that your own health and the health of your friends and neighbours demand it.

Millions of days are being lost every year through sickness which might be avoided, if only men and women would obey the laws of health. Not merely is there this immense loss, there is also the loss of the millions of dollars that are spent every year on doctors, nurses, and medicines. Moreover, the enjoyment of labour—and of recreation too—is often marred by ill health.

For all these reasons you can realize how wise it is that physiology and hygiene are prescribed subjects of study in all our schools.

Do not imagine, however, that, if you merely study this book or others like it, you will as a result grow up to be healthy men and women. You may not become anything of the sort. Knowing the laws of health and practising the laws of health are two vastly different things. A knowledge of these laws will do you no good whatever, unless it helps you to form good habits. It is only by obeying the laws of health every day you live that you may hope to grow into strong, healthy men and women, and do your daily work with pleasure and profit.

One thing is certain, that, if nations or individuals break the rules of health, they will be punished. Nature will take no excuse for not knowing the rules. She resembles a judge who punishes alike—both those who know the laws and break them, and those who do not know the laws and break them. A just judge will not allow a criminal to plead ignorance of the law.

No doubt you think that wrong-doers should be punished according as they do a little wrong, or a great wrong ; but this is not the way in which mother Nature treats us. She punishes those who know not her laws and break them, with exactly the same number of stripes as she gives those who know the laws and break them. The only ones who escape punishment are those who learn her laws and obey them.

How does Nature punish us ? Always by making us suffer pain and sickness. The pain is at first only slight —often so slight as to escape notice. Then, if we still keep on breaking her laws, more pain is put upon us ; and after some time—long or short, according to our strength—she puts an end to life. Young and old, wise and unwise, men and women, children and infants, die long before their time, and all for breaking Nature's laws.

What has been the outcome of all the pain and suffering which Nature has inflicted upon the sick and dying in bygone ages ? One result is clear: she has goaded thoughtful men to study disease to try to find out the cause. But men have been very slow to learn Nature's lessons. She has inflicted pain and suffering upon the sick and dying for thousands of years, and she is scourging men, women, and children around us every day, and yet they neglect her laws.

Grecian, Roman, and Mediæval history tells how people have died by thousands from "plagues" and "pestilences."

Nowadays we do not use these words in naming any disease. These are the older names for diseases like small-pox, yellow fever, diphtheria, and cholera, which have at different times, spread over the thickly populated parts of Asia, Africa, Europe, and America.

For example, between the years 1347 and 1368, a disease called the *Black Death* spread over Europe, carrying off about a quarter of the population, or 25,000,000 people in all. Again, in the summer of 1665, no fewer than 68,596 died in London alone of what is now known as the bubonic plague ; and ever since, diseases have swept over portions of the Old World and the New, carrying off thousands and thousands of people.

You might naturally think that people who have been beaten with Nature's terrible stripes would try to learn her laws as quickly as possible. But they do not. Even as recently as 1898, in the Spanish-American war, for one man who was killed by a bullet, four died from disease. This was no worse than what took place in many European wars. Sword and bullet slew their thousands, but disease slew its tens of thousands.

In 1902, in the war between Japan and Russia, the Japanese taught the rest of the world a lesson. For, while over 70,000 of them were killed in battle or died from the effects of their wounds, only about 15,000 died from disease. According to the old way of carrying on war, Japan should have lost 280,000 from disease. How did she manage to save all these lives? The answer is easy : her army surgeons had learned the laws of health and the officers and soldiers obeyed these laws as faithfully as they could. No bad food was eaten ; no bad water was drunk ; no infected house was entered.

How to save life during a terrible war was the lesson which Japan taught civilized Europe and America. Please remember that the American army surgeons in the Spanish-American war, and the British army surgeons in the South African war, both knew the laws of health as well as the Japanese army surgeons did ; but the American and the British soldiers did not obey the laws of health and the Japanese did.

Let me give you another example of the shameful way in which life is lost, and of how slow we are to learn the lessons which Nature tries to teach us. Only about half the babies who are born ever live to be men and women. In England, one out of every five dies within a year of its birth. In country places, and in the open and cleaner parts of cities, the death-rate is about 10 in every 100. In Ontario, in 1907, the number of babies born was 53,584 and 8,041 of these died within the first year. In different parts of the United States, the death-rate among babies is much less in country places than in towns and cities. In the crowded and unclean parts of cities, from 25 to 30 die out of every 100, in hot weather. Many of these lives can be saved. Another fact : in the United States and Canada, taken together, no fewer than 150,000 persons die every year of consumption, and yet consumption in its early stages is a curable disease.

Surely these terrible facts will make you young people bestir yourselves in order to avoid Nature's punishments of pain and death. If you go to work with a will, you can save thousands of lives. First learn Nature's laws yourselves, and obey them and try to get other people to obey them.

Every boy and girl of ten years of age can easily learn the laws of health, and understand them ; and, what is equally important, every child can help to spread a knowledge of these laws amongst other people. If only these two things were done—learning the laws and obeying them — diseases such as consumption, diphtheria, and scarlet fever would soon be almost banished from off the face of the earth.

Thus far I have been urging you to study hygiene because by so doing you can lessen human suffering and help to save human life. I now wish to say a word or two about caring for your own health.

You cannot properly take care of any one part of the body and neglect other parts. You cannot properly care for the eyes, and at the same time ill treat the brain. You cannot maintain the health of your nerves, and at the same time do injury to your muscles. There is no such thing as building up the lungs into health and strength, while the throat remains weak and unhealthy. All parts grow strong together, or all grow weak together.

A good doctor knows this, and when you go to him about any special ailment, he always—though you may not know it—studies your general health, and tries to improve it, as well as cure your particular ailment.

Forty years ago doctors used to give sick people a great deal of medicine. Nowadays they give much less, and when patients are very ill, doctors trust more to good nursing and good food than to medicines. They tell us also that the rules of health should be learned and put into practice by young folk every day they live.

## CHAPTER II

### WHAT FRESH AIR CONTAINS

In foggy weather it is easy to see that water is one of the substances in air, because the face and clothing become wet. But in clear weather it is not so easy to see that there is water in air, and yet there must be. We know that rain-water in a tub outside soon dries up ; and the water can go nowhere else than into the air, where it is invisible.

Moreover, this invisible water may be withdrawn from the air and made visible again. This is seen in summer when fine drops of water collect upon the sides of a pitcher which holds ice-cold water. People who do not know where these drops come from say that the pitcher sweats. This of course is not correct. For if the water could pass through little pores to the outside of the pitcher when it holds ice-cold water, then water should pass through these same pores when the pitcher holds warm water. But it does not.

The fact is that these drops on the outside are formed from tiny particles of water in the air which surrounds the pitcher. When the air is cooled, these particles come together and form little drops. Dew, rain, and the frost which forms on window panes in winter, all come from the water in the air,—water not in the form in which we see it in wells, rivers, and lakes, but water in the form of invisible particles.

What other substances does air contain ? Let us try to obtain an answer to this question by performing the following experiments :

Put a lump of quicklime, about as large as a hen's egg, into a quart fruit jar. Pour in water until the jar is about three-quarters full, shake it well, and allow it to stand for a few hours. By this time clear water has collected at the top, and lime is lying at the bottom. This clear water is known as lime-water. Without shaking the jar pour some of the lime-water into a small goblet or cup.

Now take a bicycle pump, or a rubber bulb syringe, and placing the end of it in the goblet of lime-water, force some of the air of the school-room through it. In the course of a minute or two, if the air in the room is very stuffy, the lime-water will gradually turn a milky colour.

Take about a half-glass of the lime-water. Now, placing one end of a glass tube, a rubber tube, or a straw in this lime-water, and taking the other end in your mouth, force air from the lungs through it. This time the milky colour appears almost immediately.

Try the experiment again with more lime-water, but in this case carry the goblet outside of the school-house, and force fresh air through it by means of the rubber bulb syringe. Notice how much longer it now takes, that is, how much more air must be passed into the lime-water before the milky colour appears.

These experiments prove to us that besides the water there is another substance in air. This second substance, like the water, is invisible and turns lime-water a milky colour. It is present in fresh air in small quantity; more of it is present in the air of the school-room; and still more of it in the air which comes from our lungs. It is known as carbon dioxide.

Then, further, the air contains oxygen—that invisible substance which is so important to our breathing. We could not live much longer than five minutes without oxygen. If it were not for this gas every animal on earth would soon die. And it is this substance which makes our fires, lamps, and candles burn. Without it they would go out at once.

Are there any other substances in air? Yes, two—nitrogen and argon—both of which resemble oxygen in being without colour, taste, or smell, and both together make up about four-fifths of the air. These two gases differ from oxygen in one very remarkable particular,—they are not necessary to keep us alive. On the contrary, if we were placed in an atmosphere of pure nitrogen or pure argon we should soon die, and if a burning lamp or candle were placed in either gas it would at once go out.

## CHAPTER III

 HOW FRESH AIR IS SPOILED

How does fresh air become impure and therefore unfit to breathe ?

Generally speaking, the air of the country is rarely spoiled. To be sure, it sometimes happens that when fires are raging over large areas of woodland country, the atmosphere does perhaps for some weeks become spoiled by smoke ; but apart from an accident like this the mass of the country air, that is, the atmosphere, is never spoiled.

It is different, however, in cities and towns, especially those in which there is much street traffic and where many shops and factories burn coal. Here the atmosphere becomes filled with smoke, dust, and frequently fine particles of filth, and the air becomes unfit to breathe.

Inside the shops, factories, and homes of the inhabitants, the air is still more unfit to breathe, because in addition to the outside impurities there are found those which come from the lungs of the inmates—men, women, and children. The smaller the houses and the more stagnant the air, the worse it becomes.

Breathing spoils the air by reducing the amount of oxygen and, at the same time, increasing the amount of carbon dioxide. It is spoiled also by tobacco smoke, by the odour of burnt food, by decaying garbage, by filthy outbuildings and yards, by bad cellars and drains, by disagreeable odours especially from the feet of people who do not bathe frequently, and by odours from the clothing, bedding, or floors and walls of houses that are not kept clean.

When the teeth, mouth, nose, and throat are all perfectly healthy, the breath has no disagreeable odour, and the air that passes out of the lungs, commonly called the expired air, is not spoiled excepting as we have seen by the loss of oxygen and the increase of carbon dioxide. But when these organs are diseased, then there are added to expired air fine particles of matter which may be not only disagreeable to the sense of smell, but also dangerous to health.

Then, again, the dirt which gathers upon clothing, and upon the outer skin of persons who do not bathe frequently, is usually in a state of decay, and gives rise to odours that are quite as disagreeable and harmful to health as are the odours from a diseased mouth, nose, or throat. ⟩

⟨ The matter which comes from the nose, throat, windpipe, skin, and lungs, as well as all other matter which comes from animals or plants, is usually spoken of as organic matter. ⟩

Lastly, there are many dust particles in the air of schools, churches, and public buildings. This dust is usually made up of fine particles of soil, soot, scales of skin, hair, bits of wool, cotton, or linen, and microbes or germs of animals and plants, so small that they cannot be seen with the naked eye. In schools, when proper care is not taken, the dust is largely increased by the particles of chalk which are brushed from the blackboards, especially when this is not carefully done.

Of course the air in public buildings does not change suddenly from being fresh air into being stuffy air. The change is a very gradual one. At 9 a.m. the air in many a school-room is no doubt perfectly fresh ; an hour or two afterwards it may be very stuffy. Whether it is so or not will depend upon the ventilation of the room.

We can nearly always tell by the smell of air whether it is fit to breathe. If it smells musty or stuffy, or has a disagreeable odour, it is unfit to breathe. It may not do a person a deal of harm to breathe bad-smelling air for a short time. If he is strong, he will soon get accustomed to the bad odour and will not mind it much ; but, if he lives for some months or years in such air, he may be quite sure that it will undermine his health and strength. It is the little harm which bad air keeps doing to us daily for years that at last breaks down health, and it is because of this that employees in shops and factories have a right to insist upon getting pure air.

While it would be very difficult to test for some of the nasty substances to be found in the expired air of a school-room, yet a rough test can be made as follows :

Take a 12 oz. bottle, such as can be obtained in any drug shop. First fill it with water and then empty the water into the school-room pail. In doing this, the air of the room will fill the bottle. Now pour into the bottle about one tablespoonful of clear lime-water and shake up and down thoroughly. If the lime-water turns milky at once, it shows that there is an excess of carbon dioxide in the air and that it is therefore unfit to breathe.

Now, the quantity of organic matter in the air increases and decreases just as the carbon dioxide increases and decreases, so that although the test given above holds true only for the carbon dioxide, yet it gives us a good idea of the quantity of the organic matter also that is present in the air of such places as school-rooms and churches.

Which of all these things in the air of an unventilated building does us most harm? Is it the lack of oxygen, or the excess of carbon dioxide; or is it the presence of decaying organic materials from the clothing, or breath?

There is some dispute among doctors as to the answers to be given to these questions, but many physicians think that, apart from disease germs, it is the lack of oxygen and the presence of organic matter from the lungs, throat, and skin that spoil the air the most.

## CHAPTER IV

X

### EFFECTS OF BAD AIR

Do people who live in bad air suffer more from ill health than those who live in fresh air? We can answer this question most satisfactorily by watching the effects of bad air upon those who have to breathe it.

Perhaps one of the most terrible instances of this was seen in the prison known as the Black Hole of Calcutta. One hundred and forty-six persons were shut up over night in a cell twenty feet square provided with no means of ventilation except two small windows. So poisonous did the air become that one hundred and twenty-three died—were suffocated—during the night.

But the effects of bad air are not often so sudden and so dreadful. Usually they are very gradual but none the less deadly. To make this clear, let us look at some statistics of the deaths from consumption which occur among soldiers who live in barracks. These men are all examined by a doctor before they are allowed to join the army. They are well-fed, well-clad, get regular exercise, live regular lives, and they should therefore continue in good health for a long time. Moreover, the rooms in which they live and sleep are all kept clean.

Of course, not all barracks are of the same size. For example, a few years ago the soldiers in the British Foot Guards had an air space of 331 cubic feet per man; whereas those in the Horse Guards had 572 cubic feet per man. In other respects both classes of soldiers had the same accommodation.

We might expect that disease and death would visit both classes alike. But such was not the case. Looking at this one disease of consumption only, we find that the deaths among the Foot Guards amounted to 14 in every 1,000 soldiers; whereas the deaths from this disease among the Horse Guards amounted to only 7 in every 1,000 men.

How is this difference to be accounted for? There appears to be only one explanation. Although the air in both barracks was stagnant and the ventilation bad, yet, as the Horse Guards had more air per man than the Foot Guards, the air did not become quite so foul, and therefore fewer of them took consumption and died.

The fact that some occupations are less healthful than others, just because of bad air, seems to be borne out by the high death-rate among barbers, hairdressers, dressmakers, seamstresses, school teachers, printers, and pressmen. The death-rate among these varies from 385 to 398 per 1,000 of those who die of all diseases, as compared with a rate of 121 to 136 among lawyers, doctors, and clergymen. There can be little doubt that the true explanation of these high death-rates is the impure air, lack of sunshine, and long hours of confinement.

When young people choose occupations which are always carried on in dusty places, such as grinding grain and making flour; spinning and weaving cotton goods; making oil-cloth and linoleum; crushing, drilling and polishing stone; cutting glass, or other similar occupations; they should see to it that not only are the hours of labour short and the wages good, but that much of their spare time is spent in fresh air and sunshine.

When dusty air is breathed for a long time, some of the particles stick to the surface of the little air sacs of the lungs, and prevent the air from passing freely into the blood. The result is, that people who have to breathe such air, suffer in health and do not live so long as those who spend their lives in an outdoor occupation.

You may understand how dust can choke up our lungs, if you look at the older and lower leaves of a buttercup or dandelion. These leaves become covered with dust and in time die, partly from the effect of the dust, partly from the shading. The dust covers over the tiny little openings on the leaves, so that they cannot breathe properly. To remedy this, the plant keeps growing new leaves above the old ones, and these new leaves can always take in enough air to keep the plant alive.

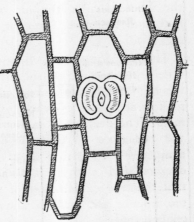

FIGURE 1.—One of the mouths on the under surface of a leaf. *A*, opening into the leaf. *B* and *C*, cells that guard the opening at *A*.

Unfortunately for us, we are not able to grow new lungs whenever we may happen to need them.

It is generally believed that the high death-rate which prevails in small houses is due to lack of fresh air, but no doubt other causes such as dirt, lack of clothing, and lack of proper food help to produce the high death-rate.

The following diagram represents the results of actual observation and shows by the relative sizes of the figures and their sub-divisions the death-rates that result from infectious diseases, nervous and nutritive diseases of children, and lung and other diseases in the case of those who live in small houses and of those who live in larger ones.

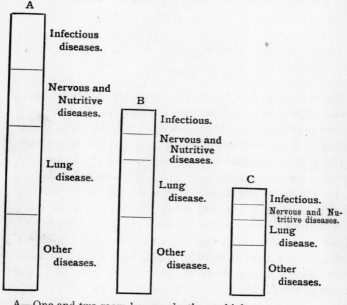

A—One and two room houses, death-rate high.

B—Two and three room houses, death-rate less.

C—Three and four room houses, death-rate still less.

The truth is that bad air in rooms, whether they are large or small, is always harmful to those who live in

them.    Spending  even  an  hour  or  two  in  such  rooms
causes  drowsiness  and  headache,  slows  down the  heart
beat, and quickens the breathing.    These effects will be
felt all the more quickly if a person is delicate.

In  a  school,  bad  air  makes  it  very  hard  for  pupils to
pay attention to what the teacher is saying.    Moreover,
it  impairs  their  health,  and  as  a  result  they  sometimes
take disease which otherwise they might escape.

---

# CHAPTER V

## VENTILATION

There is only $\frac{1}{25}$th of one part of carbon dioxide in 100
parts of fresh air.    Any increase of carbon  dioxide over
this amount therefore is regarded as an impurity.    For
example, if air contains $\frac{3}{25}$ths of carbon dioxide, then we
say that it contains an impurity of $\frac{2}{25}$ths.    It  is  usually
agreed  among  physicians  that  the  air  of  schools,
bedrooms, factories, shops or offices should not contain a
total of more than $\frac{2}{25}$ths of one part  of  carbon  dioxide.
The carbon dioxide impurity  and  the  other  impurities
in air that go with it, can be kept down to the  lowest
limits,  only  by  replacing  the  stuffy  air  of  a  room  with
fresh air.    The  question  of  ventilation  therefore  is  a
question of making air move in sufficient quantity.

What  makes  air  move ?    For  one  thing,  heat  has
much to do with it.    You can see this for  yourselves
by  simply  holding  your  hand  some  distance  above  a
stove,  a  lighted  lamp,  or  a  hot  air  register.    In  all
three cases you can feel the hot air rising against your
hand.    The air is warmed by the lamp or stove, expands,

becomes lighter than the surrounding cold air, and rises. The surrounding colder air presses in to take the place of the warm air which has risen. In its turn this air also is warmed, grows lighter, and rises in the path of the air which preceded it.

FIGURE 2.—Air moving upwards from a lighted lamp.

If we keep these facts in mind we shall not have much difficulty in understanding how some rooms become ventilated to a certain extent, even when they appear to be tightly closed up. For, all houses, since they cannot be made perfectly air tight, allow some air to pass through the stone, brick, or frame walls, and through openings around windows and doors.

Moreover, when the outside door is opened a rush of cold fresh air comes in through the lower part of the opening and a rush of stuffy air passes out through the upper part. In this way, some ventilation takes place in every house. But such ventilation is very imperfect, and never provides all the air which a family requires. We must, therefore, plan our houses so that in winter the light, warm, stuffy air shall escape through one opening and fresh air be admitted through some other opening.

How can this be done? One simple way is to arrange the window sashes so that the upper one can be lowered and the lower one raised. The stuffy air as it rises escapes at the top and fresh air comes in at the bottom. The objection to this is that those who are near the window may catch cold from sitting in a draught.

A much better way is to make the stuffy air leave a room through an outlet tube or duct which lies close to the chimney. When an outlet tube is close to a warm chimney, the chimney will heat the air in the tube and will thus make it lighter, causing it to ascend in the tube and so pass out at the top of the roof.

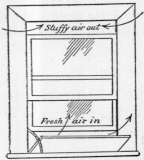

This outlet duct should open from a room at two places— near the floor, and also near the ceiling, because expired air being heavier than fresh air tends to fall to the floor,

FIGURE 3.—Slanting board, arranged so that it can be adjusted to deflect the incoming draft upward. The upper sash lowered, the lower sash raised.

especially when both kinds of air are of the same temperature. If then there is only one outlet duct near the ceiling, the foul air can not escape and must therefore accumulate along the floor.

That foul air does accumulate in this way can easily be proved by placing a candle on the floor of a crowded room in which there is little or no ventilation. In the course of an hour or so the candle will grow dimmer and dimmer, and finally go out. It will not go out at all, or at least not so quickly, if placed higher up in the room. The following experiment also illustrates this fact :—

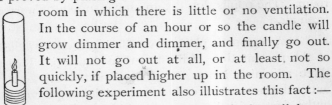

FIGURE 4.

Fit a cork into the lower end of a tall lamp-chimney so tightly that no air can enter around it. Now remove the cork temporarily and place upon it a short piece of a lighted candle. Insert the cork again and watch what happens. The candle will soon go out,—and for precisely the same reason as it will go out when placed upon the floor of an unventilated room. (Fig. 4.)

As the stuffy air escapes from a room, fresh air comes in through walls and chinks wherever it can

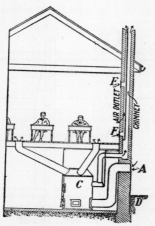

FIGURE 5.—*E* and *F*, openings into the outlet duct beside the chimney.

find entrance. Of course the quantity of fresh air that will thus enter a room cannot be sufficient for good ventilation, and so in many buildings, especially in school-houses, an inlet tube or duct is used (Fig. 5). The inlet duct, *A*, takes fresh air from the outside of the building at about five feet above the level of the ground, *D*, and conveys it to the furnace *C* in the basement where it is warmed. Thence it passes through other ducts to the school-room. The pupils thus get an ample supply of warmed fresh air.

A very common plan of ventilating dwelling-houses at the present time is illustrated in figure 6. Two or three adjoining rooms may be ventilated by separate outlet ducts—one for each room—all joining a common outlet duct which lies near the chimney.

The advantage of ventilating our houses by this system of air-flues is that the ventilation is continuous. It is spoken of as a "natural" system of ventilation to distinguish it from an artificial one, in which the air is either drawn into a room or forced out of it by ventilating fans.

Our school regulations specify that there shall be an air space of 250 cubic feet for each pupil in a school, and that this quantity of air shall be changed three times per hour, thus furnishing each child with 750 cubic feet of fresh air an hour. If we assume that 250 cubic feet more of fresh air comes into a school in winter through the porous walls and through chinks around windows and doors, we see that each child will have about 1000 cubic feet of fresh air an hour.

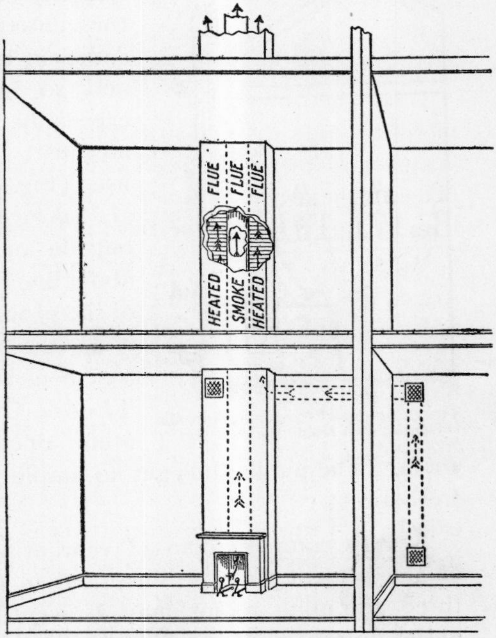

FIGURE 6.—Outlet ducts for ventilating adjoining rooms.

This, however, is often not sufficient. In some American states, school trustees are required to provide each child with at least 1800 cubic feet an hour, and this is very desirable in the interests of the health of the children.

## CHAPTER VI

### THE BURNING OF THE BODY

What becomes of all the air which enters our bodies? Well, as soon as it reaches the lungs the oxygen part passes through the thin walls of the blood-vessels and enters the blood. As the blood is circling round and round in the body all the time, the oxygen is thus carried by the blood to every part of it.

What becomes of the oxygen then? It leaves the blood through the walls of the exceedingly small blood-vessels and enters the flesh. Then the same thing takes place in the flesh as takes place in a stove or furnace, namely this, some of the flesh is burned up.

When we wish a fire to burn well, we put some wood, like cedar or pine, into the stove and turn on the draught; that is, the damper is opened so as to allow air to pass in freely. When we do this, the fire burns well; when we close the damper and keep the air from getting into the stove, the fire burns slowly. It goes out altogether if we stop the air completely.

Now, in some respects, the body is like a burning candle, or a fire. To be sure there is no flame to be seen in anyone's body; but, as you all know, there is heat.

Can we have burning without flame, and without light? Of course we can, and most people have seen this kind of burning. How does a mason make plaster? He gets a load of quicklime from a limekiln. This he puts into a large flat open box, and then he pours upon it many pailfuls of cold water. In a few minutes a hissing sound is heard somewhat like the hissing of

steam from the tea-kettle. In fact, the cold water which
the mason has poured upon the quicklime, soon begins
to boil.   If you put your hand upon the lumps of quicklime, they feel hot.   Soon afterwards, they swell up
and mix with the water and form a white liquid like
milk.   But all this time a kind of burning is going on
in the quicklime and water, which is somewhat like the
burning going on in our bodies.   There is never any
flame or light, such as may be seen in a candle, or a fire,
but there is plenty of heat.   We may say indeed that the
burning in our bodies is a kind of wet burning; it is
burning without any light and without any flame.

If we are like stoves, there should be smoke coming
off from our bodies, and there should be ashes forming
somewhere, just as in a stove.   Very true.   Two kinds
of "smoke" do come off at the top of a chimney, smoke
which we can see, and smoke which we can not see.
Now the smoke which comes off from our bodies is
smoke which we can not see.   It passes out mixed
with expired air.   It is like the smoke which passes
off from a burning candle—invisible smoke.

A burning candle can no more do without fresh air
than we can.   How long will a
candle burn without fresh air?
To get an answer, take a short
piece of candle and light it.   Now
put a glass fruit jar, mouth downwards, over the candle so as to
prevent any air from getting into
or out of the jar.   Watch what
takes place.   The flame grows

FIGURE 7.—Candle burning
under a fruit jar.

dimmer and dimmer, and then goes out altogether.

Repeat this experiment a number of times. John Mayow, the physiologist, did it often many years ago, and always with the same result. Later on in his work, in place of using a candle he used a mouse, and found that its breathing made some change in the air inside the jar which caused the animal to die.

We conclude, therefore, that a candle in burning produces something in the air that makes it unfit to keep up the burning; and that a mouse, in breathing, produces something in the air which makes it unfit to breathe again. Both candle and mouse require oxygen for their burning and both give off the invisible smoke, carbon dioxide, which poisons the air.

But what about the fuel and ashes of our bodies? If our bodies are like stoves, where does the fuel come from? We may call the food which we eat the fuel for our bodies. The food is first turned into blood and flesh, as we shall see later. Then the flesh burns by means of the air which enters our bodies, and, in burning, gives rise to heat, to invisible smoke, and to what I may call ashes.

Yes, ashes. To be sure we can not see these ashes as we can the ashes in the ash-pan of a stove; but ashes are produced nevertheless. They do not remain in the body and clog the burning, as ashes do sometimes in a furnace; but very tiny specks of ashes are forming all the time in the flesh. They are so very small that we could not find them, if we looked for them ever so carefully; but they are not so small that the blood cannot find them, and gather them all up nearly as fast as they form.

The invisible smoke is carried to the lungs and passed out in the expired air, and the ashes from the burning flesh are carried, some of them to the skin, some of them to the kidneys, and some to the intestines, and thence they are thrust out of the body. The lungs, skin, kidneys, and intestines are known as "excretory" organs, and the waste materials which they thrust out of the body are called "excretions." If the excretions, or what I have been calling smoke and ashes, were not quickly removed, we could live only a very short time.

Drinking freely of water, between meals, aids very much in the removal of the dead waste or ashes of the body. The water first enters the blood-vessels, so that more blood passes into the flesh, dissolves the waste, and helps to remove it. This is one source of the benefits which have been received by sickly people who have, in all ages, gone to drink the waters of mineral springs in different parts of the world.

The burning which goes on in our bodies does something else besides keeping them warm. It enables us to move about. Just as the burning of wood, or coal, or gasoline enables a traction engine or a locomotive or an automobile, to move from place to place, so, the burning in our bodies enables us to carry on all our bodily movements. It enables us to walk, run, work, and play. The movements of the chest in breathing, and the beat of the heart in pumping the blood, are alike caused by the burning of our bodies.

It has been calculated that about five-sixths of our food goes to form heat, and about one-sixth goes to produce bodily movements. In some respects we are like a locomotive, but we differ also vastly from one. We control and direct our own movements; but a locomotive must be run by an engineer. We see, hear, feel, and think; but an engine is only a mass of dead metal. While it is helpful, therefore, for us to think of ourselves as engines, we must remember that we are, in many other ways, something very different.

---

## CHAPTER VII

### FLOATING MATTER IN AIR

Even when the school furniture has been fairly well dusted, you can always detect some dust on it by simply wiping the surface with a clean white cloth.

Where did this dust come from? You tell me at once that it came from out of doors, and that it consists of powdered earth or stone which has been brought in on the pupils' shoes, especially when the roads are muddy. That is what Professor Tyndall thought in 1868, when he first examined the floating matter in the air of his laboratory in London. But to his surprise he found that much of this matter is composed of fine little particles which must have come from animals and plants; because, when he passed them through the flame of a spirit lamp they burned up completely, which they would not have done if they had been composed of earth or stone only.

Later on in his studies he had dust from the walls of the British Museum examined, and then he discovered that about half of it was composed of earthy matter, which, being somewhat heavy, had soon settled down on floors and walls; whereas, the other half consisted of very fine and very light particles, which had floated about in the air. Since every substance must be of animal, vegetable, or mineral origin, Tyndall concluded that the lighter inflammable particles must have come from plants or animals, and that the heavier earthy matter must have been carried from the streets on the shoes of students or visitors.

Nearly ten years before Tyndall began his experiments, Louis Pasteur had studied the composition of air, and had come to the conclusion that everywhere it contains microbes or the germs of animal and plant life. He reached this conclusion from studying the souring of milk, the fermentation of wines, and the putrefaction, or decay, of flesh; for it seemed to him that all three were due to the action of these microbes.

Up to 1860 it was generally believed that when animäl or vegetable matter began to decay there came into life, in the very act of decay, an immense number of tiny animals or plants. These living animals were believed to have sprung from dead ones. This springing into life of new forms out of dead or decaying matter was known as "spontaneous generation."

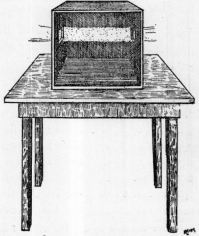

FIGURE 8.—Beam of light showing floating matter in the air of a box.

After Tyndall had read of Pasteur's experiments, it occurred to him that possibly some of these germs were to be found among the floating particles in the air of the Royal Institution, London, where he lectured. Such particles he had often noticed when a strong beam of light was passed through a darkened tube, box, or room. Unless air is unusually pure, the path of a sunbeam is always clearly marked out by a large number of dust particles moving up and down and backwards and forwards. They can generally be noticed when a magic lantern is lighted in a dark room.

You may yourselves repeat some of the experiments made by Pasteur and Tyndall, to find out the nature of these germs, if you will prepare a vegetable infusion as follows :—

Wash a turnip thoroughly in clean water, cut it into thin slices and place it in a saucepan with just enough water to cover it. Allow the whole to stand for four or five hours in a warm room. The liquid, when filtered through several sheets of filtering paper or folds of well-boiled linen, will be as clear as pure water and is known as "turnip infusion."

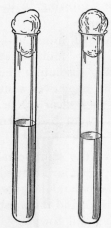

FIGURE 9.—Two test-tubes containing infusions that have been "sterilized" by boiling.

If now two test-tubes be half-filled with this infusion, plugged with what is known as sterile cotton wool, and boiled for five minutes by holding their lower ends in the upper part of the flame of a spirit lamp, the boiling will have killed all the germs that are in the liquid and in the air in the tubes above it.

If, after cooling, the cotton plug be removed for a moment from one of the tubes, and the liquid be merely touched with a needle that has been rubbed against any object in the room, the plug being again replaced, it will be found after a time that, while the liquid in this tube has turned cloudy, that in the unopened tube has remained perfectly clear and unchanged.

In Tyndall's experience, the infusions usually went bad in from three to five days, depending upon where they were placed, and especially upon the temperature at which they were kept.

Of course the apparatus which Prof. Tyndall used was not so simple as that described above. It was much more elaborate. But anybody who can procure such simple articles as two test-tubes, some sterile cotton batting, and a spirit lamp can verify for himself Pasteur's and Tyndall's conclusions about germs growing in infusions and their being killed by boiling.

Tyndall used many different kinds of infusions— mutton, fowl, hops, tea, fish,—but always found that when the infusions were exposed to air, absolutely free from dust, as tested by a beam of light, none ever went bad. They never turned sour or lost their clear colour. On the other hand, all such infusions went bad when exposed to ordinary air.

Tyndall's experiments all pointed to the same conclusions as Pasteur's, namely, that the purest air is found upon mountains, less pure air upon woodland heights, less pure air still in level farming districts, and the most impure air in crowded and dirty cities and towns.

But after Tyndall had made certain that Pasteur's experiments were correctly made, his work was by no means ended. In many of his experiments in 1875-6, he found that five minutes' boiling was sufficient to sterilize the infusions, that is, to kill the germs. Strange to say, however, the very next year. when he undertook to repeat his experiments in answer to some criticism which had been passed upon them, he was amazed to find that he could not kill the germs in the hay and other infusions short of three or four hours' continuous boiling. This puzzled him very much. But more troublous times were ahead of him.

Not merely did the hay infusions go bad, but all other kinds went bad also, even when he sought to sterilize them by continuous boiling for three hours. Four hours, however, showed a different result: the infusions then remained clear and unchanged.

Greatly puzzled, Tyndall sought to discover the cause of his failures. After many guesses, all of which he put to the test of careful experiment, he suspected that some bundles of old hay which had lain upon his laboratory floor for a year were the source of his troubles. When stirred up, this hay sent forth clouds of dust, and on making hay infusions from it he found it impossible to sterilize them short of four hours' boiling; sometimes, indeed, they required five and six, and in one case eight hours' boiling.

So thoroughly had the germs from this hay spread throughout the air of his laboratory that, when he used other infusions such as turnip or cucumber, they too, went bad, having become smitten with the plague from the hay. In short in 1876-7 it had become impossible for Tyndall to get the same results as he had got in the years 1875-6.

He, therefore, resolved to remove his apparatus to another place, and Kew Gardens were selected. Here he had no difficulty in getting the same results as he had obtained in his experiments in 1875-6.

He next tried to repeat them in a temporary shed which he had erected upon the roof of his own laboratory. But again to his surprise he failed. Not one of his infusions escaped putrefaction. On carefully considering this failure, he suspected that hay germs from his regular laboratory had been carried to the shed upon the clothing of his assistants.

On disinfecting the shed, therefore, changing the clothing of his assistants, and preventing them from passing from the laboratory to the shed lest they might carry the germs from the one place to the other, Tyndall was able to repeat successfully every experiment of his first year. With five minutes' boiling every infusion was made sterile, except of course those made from the old hay, which still required four hours' boiling.

As a result of experiments which were carried on in nearly 10,000 different vessels, Tyndall classified the germs in the air according to their power of resisting heat :—

1. Those killed under the boiling point of water.

2. Those killed in five minutes' boiling.

3. Those not killed in five minutes, but killed in fifteen.

4. Those not killed in fifteen, but killed in thirty.

5. Those not killed in thirty, but killed in an hour.

6. Those not killed in one, but killed in two hours.

7. Those not killed in two, but killed in three hours.

8. Those not killed in three, but killed in four hours.

9. Those killed by boiling over four hours.

Since Tyndall did his splendid work, it has been discovered that there are produced in the inside of some

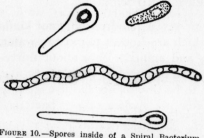

microbes very, very small, clear, rounded bodies which are known as "spores," and that these spores are much harder to kill than the parent germ. The method to-day of sterilizing infusions containing

FIGURE 10.—Spores inside of a Spiral Bacterium. Three escaped ones have started to grow.

spores is the same as Tyndall finally practised, namely, to boil the infusion for a few minutes, then allow it to stand for eight or ten hours and boil again. Boiling and cooling in this way for a number of times will sterilize the most resistant of known spores or germs.

The explanation of the effects of boiling several times at intervals seems to be that, after the first boiling, the spores which have not yet been sterilized start to grow. Before they have had time to become fully grown and to cause putrefaction in the infusion, they are boiled a second time and this kills all the spores which have sprouted as they are easily killed when in this condition. Subsequently other spores sprout, and they too are killed by the third boiling, and so on until all are killed.

## CHAPTER VIII

### DISEASE GERMS AND MICROBES

Out of between six or seven hundred different kinds of microbes or germs which are known to exist in water, earth, air, or on plants and animals, only about thirty-five cause disease in human beings. Of these thirty-five, about thirty are known to be tiny plants and five are tiny animals. The plant forms are spoken of as " bacteria," and the animal forms as " sporozoa."

The remainder of the six or seven hundred are quite harmless to health, and many are even useful.

Whether plants or animals, these tiny germs can be seen only with the aid of a powerful magnifying glass ; and, in case you have no such instrument in your school, I must just try to give you some idea of how these germs live and how they spread. This I can do best by asking you to call to mind many things which you already know about big plants and big animals.

We shall begin with some plant germs first, because they are the ones which are best known and which have been most carefully studied. Afterwards, we shall consider one or two of the animal germs.

Did you ever notice a gray or green covering on a piece of stale bread or old cheese ? If you have, then you have seen a mass of plants or moulds which belong to the same class as the plants known as bacteria. You will find them growing also on rotten fruit that has been kept in damp cellars. Often they may be seen growing on garbage in shady backyards, or on the manure heap

in barn-yards; but always in the shade.   Sunshine and
dry air kill the moulds.

Sometimes they may be found growing on boots,
shoes, and clothing in houses that have been closed

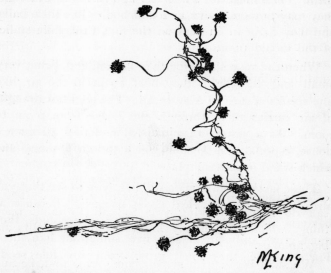

FIGURE 11.—Mould from cheese, much magnified.  The little round
knobs contain the tiny spores, or germs, of the plant.

up for some weeks in summer.   When you go into such
houses, they smell musty, and if you look closely at the
furniture, especially in the dining-room and kitchen, you
will find a fine gray bloom on almost everything—chairs,
tables, floors, walls.   No wonder the house smells musty.
When a family has been away for two months with
every door locked and every window fastened, where
have all the tiny plants come from that are found in

every part of the house? Clearly they must have grown from the spores. But where did the spores come from?

The spores are very small indeed. Even when you look closely at mouldy bread, you cannot see any of them. You must use a magnifying glass. With its aid they may be seen as small round bodies like little balls, and they hang in clusters on the fine, threadlike stalks of the mould plant.

When the spores are ripe they fall off, and, being very small and very light, they float about in the air, like fine specks of dust in a sunbeam. The slightest draught of air carries them through the house from room to room. As a result, they are to be found all over a house, especially in those in which the air is damp and which stand in a shady place.

These facts about moulds will help you to see that you already know a good deal about bacteria. Because, as bacteria are plants of the same class as moulds, they must grow and spread and live somewhat like them. For example, they must grow from invisible seeds, just as apples, or plums, or wheat, or barley grow from visible seeds. Only we do not speak of the invisible seeds of bacteria and mould as seeds; we speak of them as spores. The tiny plants themselves, or their spores, float about in the air, and when they fall upon a suitable soil, such as a piece of old bread, or meat, or jam, they begin to grow and soon produce a big crop of fresh mould and plenty of new spores.

Most kinds of bacteria will not grow upon glass, or pure sand, or in pure water. Like all plants, they will grow only when the soil is favourable. Every farmer knows that it would be of no use to sow wheat upon a rock, or upon clean sand. It would not grow on such places.

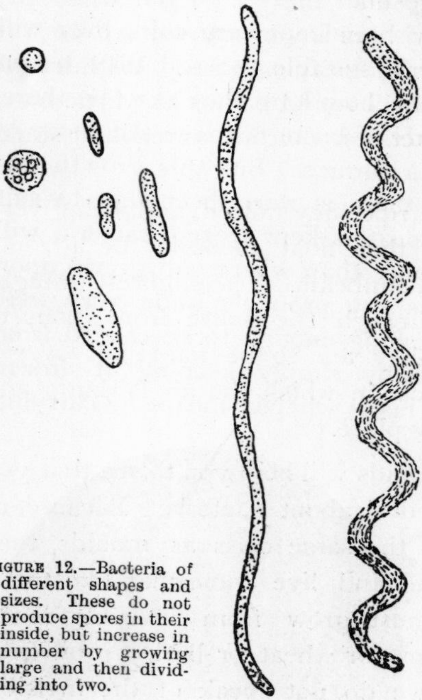

The kind of soil on which bacteria grow varies much according to the kind of bacteria. Some kinds grow upon wood ; some in earth ; some upon rocks ; some upon the teeth ; some grow upon the scalp ; some upon the skin of the body ; some upon the skin of the inside of the nose, mouth, or throat ; some upon the lining of the windpipe, or in the lungs ; some in the food while it is in the stomach or bowel ; some upon the lining of the bowel ; but wherever they grow, it is only on soil which is suitable for their growth. Warm milk is one of the best of soils for bacteria.

FIGURE 12.—Bacteria of different shapes and sizes. These do not produce spores in their inside, but increase in number by growing large and then dividing into two.

Again, other things must be suitable as well as the soil. You know that farm crops must have sufficient rain and warmth before they will grow well. And in the same way bacteria must have a certain amount of moisture and warmth to make them also grow well. Indeed, if bacteria or the spores are kept perfectly dry, they will lie for years without growing.

Then, again, if bacteria are kept very cold, they will not grow, no matter how suitable the soil may be on which they are lying nor how long they may lie there. For example, some kinds of bacteria cause the decay of meat by growing on its surface. But this growth will take place only when there is warmth enough to suit these plants. If the meat is kept frozen, bacteria will not grow upon it any more than wheat will grown upon frozen soil. In fact, as you probably know very well, meat may be preserved long enough to be carried from Australia to England by simply keeping it frozen during the voyage. This is what is meant by carrying meat or fish in "cold storage." But, just as seeds begin to grow in the spring when the weather turns warm, so the moment frozen meat is thawed, the bacteria begin to grow on its surface and the meat begins to spoil.

FIGURE 13.—The white spots denote groups of bacteria which grew from filthy milk. The plate on which these were growing was covered with a circular piece of cardboard in which the letters MILK were cut  It was then exposed to the sun, and the sunlight killed all the bacteria that were exposed.

A little while ago, I told you that moulds grow in the shade. So, most bacteria grow best in the shade. But there are other kinds which grow best in sunlight.

You know that grass does not grow well on a lawn that is much shaded with trees. It sickens and dies. You have to plant grass seed afresh every year or two on such a place. Grass grows best in bright sunshine. In the same way, some kinds of bacteria grow best in sunshine. These kinds are very useful in turning impure water into pure water. Even water that has been polluted with filth from drains or barn-yards, will, in the course of a few weeks, become pure through the effects of fresh air, sunlight, and certain kinds of bacteria.

Indeed, this is the way in which water is purified in some parts of South Africa. There, wells and springs are few in number. People, therefore, depend largely upon surface water derived from the rainfall. Now, this surface water is very likely to be polluted with filth and with a kind of bacteria which grow in filth. But, strange to say, this polluted water, when kept in open tanks and exposed to sun and air, slowly becomes pure through the growth of another kind of bacteria which flourish only in sunlight. The kind of bacteria that live upon the filth in the impure water are all killed off, and the purified filth settles to the bottom and is then quite harmless.

Then again there are bacteria which are useful in other ways. For example, the best qualities of butter and cheese cannot be made without special kinds of bacteria. Those special kinds are grown by scientific men, and sold to butter-makers and cheese-makers in order that they may be certain to make good butter and cheese in their factories.

Other bacteria which are very useful in nature are those which quickly change dead wood and the dead bodies of animals into dust. Others again are found upon clover roots, and in growing on the clover they aid very much in making the soil more fertile.

---

## CHAPTER IX

### DISEASE GERMS (*Continued*)

A very interesting thing about disease germs is that they flourish better at some seasons of the year than at others. Just as we find some plants like anemones and hepaticas producing their seed in the spring; strawberries and timothy producing their seed in early summer ; wheat and oats theirs, in July and August ; and pears and apples theirs, in October ; so we find disease-producing bacteria developing and causing disease, some at one season, some at another.

For example, diarrhœa which is due to bacteria in the bowels is most frequent in hot weather, while on the other hand, the number of cases of disease of the windpipe, bronchial tubes, and lungs, also due to bacteria, slowly increases from June to January. In the latter month there are four or five times as many people suffering from throat and lung troubles as in June.

There is a twofold reason why throat and lung troubles, and diseases like diphtheria and small-pox, are so much more prevalent in cold weather than in warm. In the first place, the cold is depressing to the health of many children and delicate people, and renders them more liable to catch infectious diseases ; and, in the second place, both sick and well people are more confined to their homes, so that disease germs spread more readily from one inmate to another.

The accompanying chart shows the variations in diphtheria in the different seasons:

| DIPHTHERIA CHART | |
|---|---|
| JAN. | ᚋᚋᚋᚋᚋᚋᚋᚋᚋᚋᚋᚋᚋ |
| FEB. | ᚋᚋᚋᚋᚋᚋᚋᚋ |
| MAR. | ᚋᚋᚋᚋᚋᚋᚋᚋ |
| APR. | ᚋᚋᚋᚋᚋᚋᚋ |
| MAY | ᚋᚋᚋᚋᚋᚋ |
| JUNE | ᚋᚋᚋᚋᚋ |
| JULY | ᚋᚋᚋᚋ |
| AUG. | ᚋᚋᚋᚋᚋᚋ |
| SEPT. | ᚋᚋᚋᚋᚋᚋᚋᚋ |
| OCT. | ᚋᚋᚋᚋᚋ ᚋᚋᚋᚋᚋ |
| NOV. | ᚋᚋᚋᚋᚋᚋᚋᚋᚋᚋᚋ |
| DEC. | ᚋᚋᚋᚋᚋᚋᚋᚋᚋᚋᚋᚋ |

In one other point bacteria resemble big plants. As you know, after seeds are planted in the spring, they remain in the soil for some days before they show any signs of sprouting; but if the soil is moist and warm, the seeds are in reality growing all the time, though they show no signs of coming up. In almost precisely the same way disease-producing bacteria remain some time in the body before they cause any marked signs of the disease. The time during which the germs appear to lie quiet varies much in different diseases, as you will see from the following table:—

| | Time from Exposure to First Sign of Disease. | | Time from Exposure to First Sign of Disease. |
|---|---|---|---|
| Measles............ | 7-14 days | Whooping-cough.... | 7-14 days |
| German Measles.... | 10-14  " | Mumps ............ | 7-21  " |
| Diphtheria........ | 1-8  " | Chicken-pox........ | 10-14  " |

Hitherto I have been speaking of diseases that are caused by tiny plants ; let us now look briefly at one or two diseases which are caused by tiny animals. And first let us consider the facts about malarial fever.

We read of this disease in the times of the ancient Romans. A few miles from the city of Rome there is a large tract of marshy land. Many generations of people living near it have suffered from malarial fever. At certain seasons of the year the disease is very prevalent. The peasants are as much used to the coming of this disease every year as they are to the coming of cold weather or hot weather. They think the disease is caused by the heat and dampness. A white vapour they say oozes out of the soil, and when this is breathed, people take the fever.

But in 1900 a strange thing happened. Two scientific men built a cottage on one of the dampest parts of the tract, and lived in it all summer and autumn, but they did not catch the fever. They had gone to Italy solely to test the truth or the falsity of an idea which they had about the cause of the disease. Their idea was that the disease was caused by germs getting into the blood, and that when a mosquito sucked such germ-laden blood from a person who had malarial fever, and afterwards sucked blood from a well person, the mosquito in doing so gave the germs to the well person. In short, they thought that the mosquito was the carrier of malaria germs.

Accordingly, they screened their cottage windows and took care not to be bitten by mosquitoes, and they really did escape the disease. But to make sure that their idea was right, they sent to England some mosquitoes which had bitten malarial patients in Italy. When these insects reached England and were allowed to bite a healthy person, he caught the disease just the same as if he had been in Italy.

As soon as this became known wise people everywhere have been filling up marshes and ponds and thus trying to prevent malaria by killing off the special kind of mosquito which spreads this fever. The kind which spreads it is known as *Anopheles.*

This disease is not caused by bacteria, which as you now know are plants, but by a very tiny animal, which passes part of its life in a mosquito, and the other part in the blood of a human being. Hence, "no mosquito, no malaria; no man, no malaria."

It is believed that the germs of yellow fever, a very fatal disease and one much dreaded in the West Indies and the southern United States, are carried by another kind of mosquito—*Stegomeyia.* At any rate, the recent outbreaks of this disease have all been successfully fought by securing great cleanliness and by avoiding mosquito bites.

|  | Time from Exposure to Signs of Disease. |  | Time from Exposure to Signs of Disease. |
| --- | --- | --- | --- |
| Malaria | 10-30 days | Scarlet Fever | 1-7 days |
| Yellow Fever | 2-15 " | Small-pox | 12 " |

There is much more doubt as to the cause of scarlet fever and small-pox. Some medical men believe that these diseases also are caused by animal germs, but they

are certainly not carried by mosquitoes. They seem
rather to spread through the air from germs which are

FIGURE 14.—The statue of Dr. Jenner. Erected to commemorate his great discovery
that a person becomes immune to small-pox by undergoing vaccination.

discharged from the nose, eyes, and mouth, and from big
pimples, or peelings from the skin.

## CHAPTER X

### HOW GERMS SPREAD

Let us now try to understand how disease germs are spread. But first let me ask you how plant seeds are spread.

You have often seen the downy seeds of the dandelion and of the thistle carried along in the wind. Or you may have noticed burs sticking to the hair of a dog, the wool of a sheep, or the tail and mane of a horse. The hard seeds of currants and berries are often seen in the droppings of birds. On one occasion Charles Darwin got no fewer than 80 seeds to sprout from a small piece of mud which he had removed from a bird's foot. In all these cases, seeds may have been carried a long distance from the plant or shrub on which they grew. The seeds of many common plants are also scattered by winds, waves, tides, streams, animals, ships, and railway cars ; and as seeds are scattered, so the germs of infectious diseases are scattered in the air, in water, in dust, in food, in clothing, by means of dirty bank-notes, and by means of animals, such as house-flies, mosquitoes, horses, dogs, cats, rats, cattle, and, of course, by man himself, especially by those who have been in contact with infected persons.

Keep these facts firmly in your mind when you think of the spread of diseases such as measles, whooping-cough, scarlet fever, mumps, diphtheria, chicken-pox, small-pox, and that most terrible scourge, consumption.

Let us now consider more particularly how two infectious diseases, scarlet fever and typhoid fever, are spread.

Some parents think that when one child in a house takes scarlet fever or diphtheria, they can prevent the disease from spreading to other children by simply

FIGURE 15.—A crowded street-car helps to spread an infectious disease throughout a city.

keeping the sick child in one room. And, indeed, they might if they were very careful. If the mother or nurse never left the sick room; if the door were kept closed or carefully screened all the time; if every article that left the sick room each day were first disinfected with strong chemicals or in boiling-hot water; if, after the child was well, the room and everything in it—floor, walls, windows, furniture, carpet, curtains, and bed-clothes,—were also thoroughly disinfected; and, finally, if the child and nurse were first bathed, and then passed to an adjoining room and there supplied with a complete change of clothes, there would be some chance of confining the disease to one child in the family.

Many parents are foolish enough to think that all this care is unnecessary. They therefore neglect some of these precautions, with the result that the disease spreads to every child in the family.

Not many years ago, when any infectious disease was spreading through a family, kind neighbours used to visit the house and help to nurse the sick ; and not knowing how infectious diseases are spread, these neighbours would return to their own homes, without ever once thinking about disinfecting their clothes or washing their hands and faces. In this way they carried the disease germs to their own homes, and so the disease would spread over a large district.

In order to prevent this, a law has been made requiring a notice to be posted over the door of every house in which there is an infectious disease. In compliance with this law, you will sometimes see on a house a card with the words : " Scarlet Fever," " Small-pox," or "Diphtheria." This card not only warns people not to enter the house, but it implies that the children in the house should not go to day-school or to Sunday-school ; and that grown-up folk belonging to the house should not mingle with others at " bees " or thrashings, or in shops, factories, street-cars, or churches.

You may think this law is a cruel one, because it keeps people from visiting the sick and afflicted ; but in reality it is a wise and just one ; for it warns people to keep away from disease germs, and it thus helps to stop the spread of disease.

The following diagram shows the results in a certain number of scarlet fever cases.

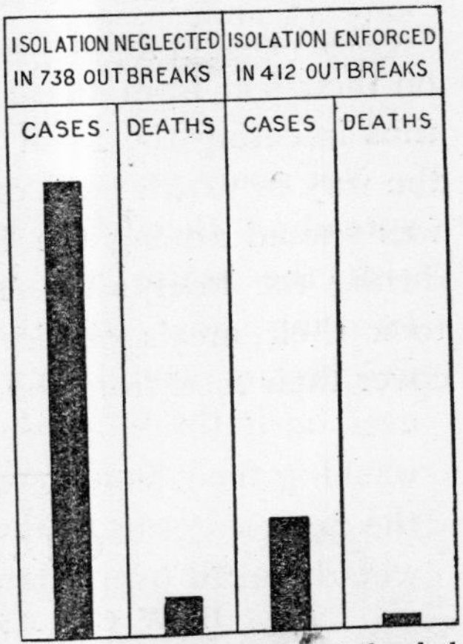

You see at once how very greatly the number of cases decreased when the sick were kept separate from the well. Keeping them separate is known among doctors as "isolation."

Now, isolation is not a cruel thing. It is the kindest thing that can be done when you look at the matter from all sides; but isolation of the sick does not keep us from helping them. It forbids us to go into a house where there is an infectious disease; but, it does not prevent us from paying a nurse to wait upon the sick, or sending food and clothing to those who are in need of these things.

FIGURE 16.—The lengths of the dark columns show how isolation and disinfection have lessened the spread of scarlet fever.

A few words about typhoid fever. It is usually caught through drinking filthy water; that is, water into which the germs of typhoid have passed. More rarely it is spread through infected milk. Again when dirty people live in close contact with one another and one of them catches the disease, it spreads from him to others, the germs being carried on the hands. Even among cleanly people it is spread in this way, unless the utmost care is taken.

Then, too, when the discharges from typhoid patients are emptied, without disinfection, into common privy vaults, there is great danger of flies carrying the germs on their feet from these places to the dining-room, and thus infecting the food. This is believed to have been the way in which most of the typhoid, or "enteric" fever, was spread among the British soldiers in South Africa during the Boer war. The soldiers lived in tents and took their meals outside, and hence it was difficult to cover their food from the flies.

## CHAPTER XI

### HOW GERMS CAUSE DISEASE

Some of you are no doubt wondering how these germs cause disease ; but if you keep your eyes open to many facts that are about you, you will not find it difficult to understand.

Have you ever noticed dark blotches on the skin of an apple ? If you have, you have seen a disease that is caused by a plant closely related to bacteria. We cannot say that the apple tree is sick, or that it has a fever or suffers pain ; but we can truthfully say that the apples are diseased. Such fruit will not keep as long as that which is free from blotches. It soon begins to decay just where the blotches are. Every fruit grower knows this very well, and in the spring he takes great pains to spray his trees with a mixture of chemicals that will kill the microbes which cause this disease.

Or, take another example. Have you ever seen a tree, part of which was alive, and part dead? A boy may have chopped off some of the bark from the tree and exposed the soft sappy wood underneath. Then something like this took place. Microbes from the air fell upon this tender, moist wood, began to grow, and in the very act of growing caused the death of the underlying wood. It does not always follow, of course, that the whole tree dies. Only that part may die which is close to where the cut was made.

FIGURE 17.—Tree rotten on one side.

In much the same way, disease germs, in growing on the human body or inside of it, make changes in the flesh and blood that are like the changes in the rotting wood of a tree. In growing, the germs form poisons called "toxins." Some of the flesh decays and the blood becomes poisoned just where the bacteria are growing. Then this poisoned blood circulates all through the body, the person becomes hot, and is said to be in a fever.

Moreover, if the changes in the flesh and blood are very great, the person has much pain and fever, and becomes unable to eat. Then, between the pain and fever, and the loss of appetite, he grows very ill and weak, and at length dies, unless the disease is cured or cures itself, as sometimes happens.

You will now be able to understand what is meant by "catching" a disease. Of course, you cannot really catch any disease. What you can catch are disease germs— from air, water, food, and the thousand and one other objects which you may happen to touch or handle. Sometimes they enter the body by a scratch, cut, or pimple. The germs are said to "infect" the body, and the pain, swelling, redness, and fever are the signs that the germs are increasing in number and destroying the tissues of the body.

The diseases which are spread in this way are said to be "infectious" diseases. A few years ago we used to speak of some diseases as infectious and others as contagious. This latter term is old-fashioned and should be dropped altogether. "Contagion" means that germs are conveyed from one person to another in one special way, namely, by touch or contact; but all contagious diseases are also infectious ; that is, both are caused by microbes.

The old idea that disease germs spring from filth must be completely abandoned. We know of no case in which disease has been caused by filth itself. It is quite true that filth of various kinds is the food or soil upon which disease germs grow; but the germs themselves, whose presence in the filth causes the disease, must first have been planted there from somewhere else.

Wheat grows on a field only when wheat has been sown on the field ; and, in the same way, disease germs of any kind grow on food or in the garbage heap only when the germs of that kind have been sown there.

Thus scarlet fever germs spring from scarlet fever germs and from no other source, and the germs of typhoid fever from the germs of typhoid fever and from no other source.

There is no mystery about the spread of many diseases if you will but remember that they are caused by the growth of minute parasitic plants or animals whose invisible seeds must come from some parent source. As Florence Nightingale long ago expressed it, the germs of each contagious disease reproduce themselves just as naturally and certainly as if they were cats or dogs.

How is it that some people catch infectious diseases, while others do not? It never happens that every person in a city or country district takes consumption or typhoid fever or the plague. Some always escape. Why?

We shall return to this subject later, but for the present it will be enough to say that the germs of certain diseases will not grow readily in some people, while they do grow readily in others. Some people are born with bodies vigorous enough to kill the invisible seeds which alight upon them; others are not so born. Then again, people are very liable to catch infection when they are run down in health; whereas, when they are vigorous, they may suffer no harm from disease germs.

Three things, therefore, are necessary before we can catch an infectious disease. First, there must be the germ; secondly, this germ must enter the body in some way; and thirdly, we must be in such a condition as to take the disease, either because we are naturally liable to it or because we are in a state of poor health.

## CHAPTER XII

### HOW TO AVOID INFECTION

We can avoid infection from disease germs in three ways :—(1) by being clean in our person, clothing, homes, and surroundings ; (2) by killing the germs by means of boiling water or by the use of chemicals known as disinfectants ; and (3) by taking care to keep our health up to a high standard of perfection.

FIGURE 18.—A Floor that is difficult to keep clean.

Professor Lister, of Edinburgh, was the first surgeon in the world to make use of Pasteur's idea that the air contains the germs of disease. After reading about Pasteur's work and that of men engaged in similar experiments, it occurred to Lister that if he could only keep the germs in the air out of surgical wounds they would heal up much more quickly than was usually the case. He, therefore, began to perform all of his surgical operations under a spray of weak carbolic acid, so that any germs that might fall from the air into the wound would be killed. The result was that in his hospital practice, even in the midst of surroundings that were reeking with the germs of blood-poison, erysipelas, and gangrene, he was able to keep his patients free from these terrible scourges.

To-day surgeons do not perform any difficult or dangerous operation in the wards of a general hospital.

The risks are too great. Nor do they use Lister's
method of spraying wounds, though they use his prin-
ciple of protecting the wound from germs.
They have what is known as an operating
room, and this room as well as the instru-
ments, the surgeon's hands and his clothing,
the nurse and her clothing, and all the linen or
cotton dressings, are kept so clean that to-day
it is a rare thing for the germs of any disease
to find lodgment in a wound. If, indeed, a
surgeon could perform his operations in a
perfectly dustless atmosphere; that is, in air
from which the germs had been perfectly
filtered, he could achieve even greater success
than Lord Lister did with his carbolic acid
spray.

Keeping in mind the facts about disease
germs being in air and on almost everything
we touch or handle, it follows that there are
some practices, common in many schools and
homes, which should be at once stopped.
For example, the practice of having a number of pens and lead pencils kept in a box,
and passed round to pupils from day to day,
is wrong; because some pupils have the
habit of holding these articles in the mouth.
The next time they are passed round the

FIGURE 19—End
of a lead pencil
bitten by dif-
ferent pupils.

class, other pupils in turn place them in their mouths,
and the result is that disease is sometimes spread from
pupil to pupil. Then, too, the common drinking cup
should be banished. Each child should have his own
cup, hanging ready for use below his desk, and, when he

is thirsty, he should go to a water pail fitted with a cover and tap, and draw the water directly into his cup ; or, if there is a well upon the school grounds, he should draw the water from the pump.

Wash-basins and towels are provided in many schools for the use of the pupils. As a rule no harm comes

FIGURE 20.—Drinking cups at a public fountain are sometimes a means of spreading disease.

from their common use. In lumber camps and factories also, a common wash-basin and a common towel are used for months at a time without any great harm being done. But cases are well known in which horrible diseases, particularly of the skin, have spread from one dirty person to others through the use of a common towel. It is much better, therefore, to err on the side of safety, and to avoid using towels, combs, brushes, and pencils which have been used by a number of people.

You may learn how thoughtful men and women look at this matter if you visit the wash room of a first-class hotel or of a Pullman car. There you will find that each guest or passenger is provided with a separate towel, and uses his own soap, comb, and brush.

In order to avoid infectious diseases it is a good rule, when you are travelling, to stay only at those hotels which are kept scrupulously clean. This will cost you a little more money, but it may be much the cheaper plan in the end ; because, if by staying at an uncleanly hotel, you should happen to catch diphtheria or scarlet fever or consumption, or if you should carry the invisible seeds of one of these diseases to some one at home, it would cost yourself or your relatives vastly more money in the end than if you had stayed at a first-class hotel.

Then again, when you are away from home, you should be careful to send your washing out to be done in a clean house or laundry. As a rule, it is safer to have washing done in a laundry than in a private house. The manager of a laundry is usually careful to disinfect all clothing that is sent to him ; that is, he soaks the clothing in a solution of some chemical such as carbolic acid or bichloride of mercury. He leaves the clothing for a considerable time in these chemicals in order to make certain that all disease germs have been killed. Or, instead of disinfecting the clothes by means of chemicals, he may use boiling-hot water or steam. When clothing has been well boiled, there is no danger of any of the work-people in the laundry catching any disease from it.

Nor, on the other hand, is there any danger of disease spreading from the laundry to private houses, unless some of the workers in the laundry bring disease germs from their homes, and handle the clothes after they have been dried and ironed.

As regards washing that is done in our own homes, no special care need be taken with it, if there is no infectious disease among members of the family. But, if any one in a family is suffering from an infectious disease, then the greatest care should be taken, not merely in washing the clothing but in handling it.

You must never forget that liquid discharges of every kind, whether from the eyes, ears, nose, mouth, throat, lungs, intestines, or skin of persons suffering from infectious diseases, may contain the germs of these diseases and are therefore dangerous. Some discharges are dangerous when moist, but they are doubly dangerous after they become dry. Because, when they are deposited upon the floor, upon handkerchiefs, bed-clothes, or wearing apparel, they dry up, and the germs in the dried discharges are very easily scattered through the air and give the disease to other members of the family.

In avoiding infectious diseases, it is important that you take such good care of your health that you will always be strong and fit for your work. When you are in robust health, you will escape a disease like consumption, which you may catch when you are run down in health. For, you must never forget that your bodies—both inside and outside—are the soil on which disease germs grow.

If the juices of your bodies are in a healthy state, they will generally kill disease germs, and you will

escape infectious diseases in this way. What are these
juices you may ask? They are the fluids which form
naturally on the lining of the nose, mouth, throat, windpipe, stomach, and bowels. If the germs are not killed
by these juices and happen to get into the blood, then
the blood or other fluids in the body, if they are well-
nourished and healthy, may do the killing.

But, if you are run down in health through poor
food or overwork or worry or lack of rest and sleep,
then every part of your body—juices, blood, flesh and

FIGURE 21.—A Neat Outbuilding for a School.

all, falls into a bad state and loses its power of killing
disease germs. People in this run-down state take
various diseases which people who are in good health
escape.

We may sum up then by saying that the first great
rule in avoiding infectious diseases is to be clean ourselves and to keep our surroundings clean; and the
second great rule is to keep the health up to a high
standard. Stop working altogether when you are feeling
"under the weather" and unfit to do your daily work.
Rest and good food will make you strong and robust in
a few days or weeks, and you can return to your work
again, feeling that, excepting in case of accident, you

will escape all infectious diseases, if you should happen
to be exposed to them.   But you should never neglect

FIGURE 22.—Untidy Outbuildings.

to take ordinary precautions to prevent the transmission
of disease germs from others to yourself, and also from
yourself to others.

# CHAPTER XIII

### HAIR

Two kinds of hair are found growing on the human
body.   The first is the hair of the head and face.   The
second is the fine short hair which can be found growing
on the arms, chest, and other parts of the body.   It is
easily seen on the back of the hand.   It is shorter,
thinner, and finer than ordinary hair or whiskers, and
grows very slowly during our lifetime.   In some people
it is so fine and short as to be almost imperceptible,
while in others it is so long and thick as to resemble
that which grows on the bodies of some animals.

A single hair, whether of the head or of the body,
grows out from the bottom of a little tube or "follicle"

which dips down into the skin and which can be seen only with the aid of a microscope. Each hair gets its food from little blood tubes or vessels; has a nerve thread running up to the root; has a small muscle joined to its side; and lastly, each has a little bag-like gland which sends out a kind of oil along the side of the hair. So we see that the two kinds of hair are very much alike.

Perhaps the strangest thing about hair is that each one should have a little muscle joined to the side of the root. What is the use

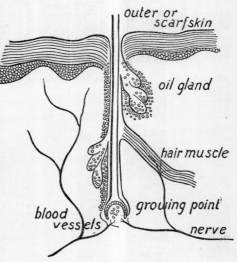

FIGURE 23.—Hair in its follicle.

of this muscle? We know that wherever we find a muscle in any animal, it has only one use. It makes the parts of the animal move. But who ever saw a man's hair moving? The old poet Virgil tells us that the hair on Aeneas's head stood on end the night the city of Troy was captured by the Greeks; and we often hear of similar cases—the hair on a person's head standing up through fear or on account of some very strange sight; but these cases are in reality very rare, and only a few persons have ever seen them.

A very common sight, however, is that of the hair
standing upright on a dog's back as he meets a
strange dog.   Now, just as the hair on a dog's back is
made to stand almost on end by means of the little
muscles at the side of each hair, so the hair muscles in a

FIGURE 24.—Dogs.   One with hair erect on its back.

person's skin, when they contract or shorten, must make
the hairs move even though a very little.

I wonder how many boys or girls, in taking a cold
bath, have noticed the little rounded knobs that form on
the skin.   They are known as "goose-flesh," because they
look like the little knobs that may be seen on the skin
of a plucked goose.   If you look closely at these knobs
or points on the human skin, you can see that they run in
rows or curved lines, just like those on the goose.   These

rows are known as "hair tracts," and they occur on the skin of many animals besides man. These hair tracts are best seen in the monkey, bear, or any other animal that has coarse hair growing on its body.

Now, what is it that makes goose-flesh form on the human skin when it becomes cold? Just this: the little hair muscle shortens or contracts, and raises the skin into a little point. The hair itself must move also, but the movement is so slight that you cannot notice it unless you watch very closely.

Hairs are joined to the skin only at the very bottom of the hair tube, at a point known as the *growing point*. The growing point has a rich supply of blood, and it is from the blood that the material comes out of which hair is made. When the growing point dies the whole follicle dies, and all the "hair restorers," "hair tonics," or "hair oils" in the world can not make the hair grow again.

When a hair is pulled out from the scalp of a young person in good health, another will grow in its place if the growing point is not killed. Hair that falls out, as it sometimes does, merely from want of proper care, or after a serious illness, will grow again of its own accord if the scalp is properly cared for.

FIGURE 25.—Touching hair on the back of the hand with a lead pencil.

Two different kinds of nerve fibres, or threads, are joined to the root of a hair. One of these carries messages from the upper part of the spinal cord to the blood-vessels at the root, so that they widen or narrow in bore and thus increase or lessen the amount of blood supplied to each hair.   Rubbing or massaging the scalp stirs up these nerves so that they cause more blood to flow to the scalp.   The increased blood-flow nourishes the growing point and promotes a vigorous growth of hair.

The other kind of nerve fibre carries messages from the root to the brain, so that even when any very light thing touches a hair we know it almost at once inasmuch as these minute nerve fibres are very sensitive.   We may conclude, therefore, that while the use of ordinary hair and whiskers is to protect the head, face, and neck, the use of the hair on the body is to act as an organ of touch.   In the case of the hairy Ainos, however, upon whom the hair grows thick and long, its use is evidently to protect the body from the cold in winter and from the heat in summer.

FIGURE 26.—Hairy Aino.
(From Wiedersheim's *Structure of Man.*  By permission of Macmillan & Co., London.)

Hair begins to turn gray first upon the temples.   In most people, gray hairs show themselves at about forty years of age.   Some people, however, turn gray about twenty-five, and others not until fifty-five or sixty.   The cause of gray hairs is the failure of the growing point to form the colouring matter which gives colour to the hair.   At forty-five or fifty the hair begins to fall out, and thenceforward it is never so thick as in early life. The change in colour and thickness marks a gradual loss of bodily strength, not merely in the skin but in the whole body. When a man is sixty years of age, white thin hair tells him as plainly as words can that his bodily powers have begun to fail.

The colour of a man's hair, its coarseness or fineness, the fact of its falling out early in life or turning gray at thirty or thirty-five years of age, are all generally explained by saying that he inherits these peculiarities from parents or near relatives. But whether a man is descended from a gray-haired or a bald-headed family or not, he should take great care of his hair.

No hair tonic can be applied and no rules can be followed which will prevent hair from turning gray; but by washing the hair weekly or fortnightly, and by massaging and brushing the scalp for a few minutes two or three times a day, the hair can be prevented from falling out for years. What is meant by massage will be explained more fully later on.

Tight, heavy hats or caps, impede the circulation of the blood in the scalp and tend to make the hair fall out. Pulling upon the hair when combing out tangles or putting it up in curl papers, also tends to make it fall out by injuring the growing point or by causing its death.

## CHAPTER XIV

### THE SKIN

Most young people know that the outer layer of the skin, that is the scarf skin, does not hurt when it is pricked with a pin, or cut with a sharp knife ; and they know also that, when a blister forms, a drop or two of a watery liquid collects between this outer skin and the true skin beneath. After this watery liquid dries up, the outer coat may be peeled off without causing any pain.

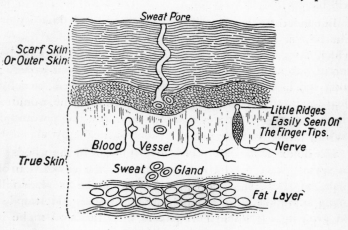

FIGURE 27.—The Skin.

But there is one thing about this outer coat which many people do not know. Like hair and nails, it is growing toward the surface all the time. Why then does it not become thicker and thicker like the bark of some trees ? The answer to this question is that the skin is slowly peeling off at the surface every day we live.

In most people the rate of growth is about the same as the rate of peeling, and therefore the thickness remains about the same. This is also true of the bark of some trees. But with people who never take a bath, the skin thickens and becomes covered with a crust of dirt as well. This does serious harm to the health, although the harm does not come upon such people all at once. If a person is very strong, it may take years before he suffers very much from allowing his skin to grow thick and dirty. Slowly and surely, however, he will have to pay for his folly.

But before telling how this will come about, I should like to ask if there is any other animal besides man which casts off its skin. If you have ever kept frogs in a tub of water for a few weeks you will know. You would soon see flakes of skin, as large as a five-cent piece, floating in the water. A turtle in confinement would show very much the same thing, only the flakes would be larger and thicker.

No doubt some boys who love to roam in the woods in spring, have seen the cast-off skin of a snake. In place of shedding their skin in fine scales as we do, many snakes shed their outer skin all at once. It keeps on growing for some months and afterwards comes off without causing them any pain.

We shed ours little by little, in bits so small that we scarcely notice them. Flakes of skin, so small as to need a magnifying glass to see them, stick to our underclothing, or come off when we wash our face and hands or take a bath. This skin is dead and useless, and should be removed in order to keep the body strong and healthy.

Why must it be removed ? No doubt there are people who have never bathed and who nevertheless seem to be in good health. A disagreeable odour generally comes from the sweat and clothing of such people. This bad odour arises from the decaying scarf skin as well as from the sweat.

As everyone knows, sweat, or perspiration, comes away from the skin when we are too warm. It comes away also when we are not warm at all. You may prove this for yourselves by placing your hand up to the wrist in a large widemouthed bottle. The bottle must be dry and cool. In a half minute or less a little mist forms on the inside of the bottle. This is the invisible sweat which is coming from the small pores or openings in the skin of the hand.

FIGURE 28.—The hand in a bottle showing moisture forming from the sweat-pores.

If we should cut open one of these pores and examine its inner end with a magnifying glass, we should find the small rounded body which made the sweat. It is called a sweat-gland. There are probably between one and two millions of these glands in the human skin. The quantity of sweat given off from them daily is very great, varying between one and four pints. It is very difficult to measure the quantity exactly, because it varies from time to time with the kind of food, the quantity of fluid drunk, the temperature of the air, the season of the year, and the work done by other organs besides the sweat-glands, such as the lungs and the kidneys.

About one-third of an ounce of the daily output of sweat is salt and other substances, the rest being, of course, water. With the watery part of sweat we are not at present concerned ; but, as we shall see later, its chief use is to keep us cool when we are too warm. When this watery part dries up it leaves behind it on the surface of the skin the salt and other substances of which we have just spoken. Water, on the other hand, which has been spilt upon the floor dries up, we know, and disappears, but pure water leaves no trace behind it.

Where does this solid matter in sweat come from ? In answer, it may be said that the sweat-glands obtain it from the blood, and the blood obtains it from the flesh, bone, nerves, and other parts of the body.

The salt and other matter in the sweat is in fact dead stuff which the blood gathers up from all over the body and carries to the sweat-glands to be thrown off through the pores. It is in reality a kind of poison. If the dead skin be not removed from the body by bathing and rubbing, the sweat-pores will get clogged up and the new skin, which lies below the crust of dead skin and dirt, will become choked. This is bad for one's health. ✗

Dirty skin is bad for another reason. It forms a suitable soil on which the invisible seeds of disease may grow. Ringworm is a disease that is caused by invisible seeds, and it occurs on the skin of the arms, body, or scalp. The germs spread from one dirty person to another, and even to a clean person if he touches the skin or clothing of one who has ringworm. Not only must we be clean ourselves, therefore, but we must take care not to touch a dirty person, or anything which he handles.

In the same way, the disease called the itch spreads from one person to another. This disease is caused by a very small animal, like a spider, which gets upon the skin from some one who has the itch. The animal lays its eggs under the skin and these cause little sores that become very itchy. The disease may be caught by shaking hands with people who have the itch, by sleeping in their beds or by handling objects which they have used.

From what you now know about the sweat-glands and the skin, you will see that you must practise cleanly habits if you wish these organs to get rid of the dead and poisonous materials that are always forming in the body, and if you wish also to provide against annoying diseases.

Strong people should bathe in cool water (about 80° F.) every morning. So should delicate children and aged people if they can stand the cold, but if they cannot they should use tepid water (about 90° F.). The best soap should always be used in taking a bath. Bad soap injures the skin.

If there is no bathroom in a house, the whole body should be sponged, or rubbed over with a towel or linen mitten dipped in cool water. This should be followed by brisk rubbing with a coarse towel.

Once a week before going to bed a warm bath (about 100° F.) should be taken. This removes portions of the scarf skin which are not readily removed by cold water even with the aid of soap.   Moreover, for evident reasons, all underclothing should be changed at least once a week and invariably taken off at night and hung up to air.

The nails should be cut regularly with a pair of scissors, the shaping being rounded like the end of the finger.   No cleanly person ever allows dirt to accumulate beneath his nails, and no cleanly person ever bites off the tips of his nails.   The habit of biting the nails, if kept up for some years by a child, results in the ends of the fingers becoming blunt, rounded, and ugly.

## CHAPTER XV

### THE NOSE AND THROAT

The nose is of great use to us in other ways than in enabling us to smell.   It warms, moistens, and cleanses the inspired air.   For example, when we are travelling in dusty cars, the nose stops much dust from passing down the throat and into the lungs.   It gathers in a ring at the entrance to the nostrils.   The same thing may be noticed in men who have been working close to a thrashing-machine or who have been shovelling coal.

The nose stops also many of the invisible germs of disease from passing down the throat.   In fact, the nose is more useful to us in this silent work of keeping out dust and disease germs than it is as the organ of smell.

When you open your mouth and by means of a mirror look toward the back of it, you see your throat. But there is another passage into the throat besides the one from the mouth.   The two nostrils join each other about one and a half inches from the tip of the nose, and open by one passage into the throat behind. The large chambers just inside of each nostril are for use in

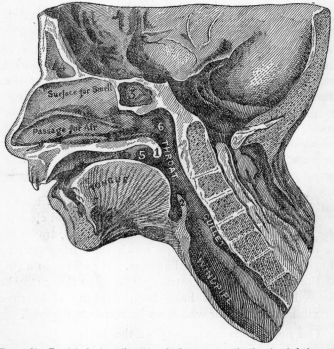

FIGURE 29.—Front to back section through the nose, mouth, throat, wind-pipe and gullet. 1, the uvula; 2, the epiglottis which covers the opening into the wind-pipe; 3, an opening in the bone; 4, an opening in the forehead bone; 5, the back part of the mouth; 6, the upper part of the throat, into which the nose passages open.

smelling; the passages backward into the throat are for breathing.

Lying under the skin which lines the inside of the nose, mouth, and throat, are a large number of small

organs somewhat like sweat-glands.    In these glands
juices are forming all the time.   When in a healthy
condition, the juices kill the disease germs which
may happen to enter the nose along with the dust.
Even when there are no disease germs to kill, the
juices catch the dust and germs, and pass them out
at the mouth or nose.

It is very important that there should be a free and
open passage for the air from the front opening of the
nose right back to the throat.   Sometimes in children
the paired nostrils, just where they join and enter the
throat, become closed up by growths of soft flesh, called
"adenoids," so that the child cannot breathe through
its nose.    Its breathing must accordingly be done
through the mouth.    Now this mouth-breathing, as it is

called, is very bad, because the dust
and invisible germs in the air can not
be stopped so well as in the nose
passages.   If, therefore, we breathe
through the mouth, there is great
danger of catching certain kinds of
disease.

Besides this, mouth-breathing
causes the teeth to stick out and

FIGURE 30.—Face of a
mouth-breather.

spoils the shape of the mouth.    If you find out,
therefore, that you breathe through your mouth instead
of through your nose, you should lose no time in seeing
a doctor and asking him to provide a remedy.

The best advice that can be given about caring for the
nose and throat is to avoid catching cold.   "Bad colds,"
which are known also as "la grippe," or "influenza,"

are usually caused by bacteria. These bacteria do not usually grow in a healthy nose or throat, but they do start to grow very readily in throats that have been chilled by cold moist winds. If one is out in such weather for a long time, the cold drives the blood away from the throat and inner surface of the nose, and unless one is hardy, a "cold" is the result.

When we catch cold the lining of the nose or throat becomes red, swollen, hot, and more or less painful. That it is red and swollen may be seen at a glance by simply opening the mouth as wide as possible, facing a window, and then examining the throat by means of a looking-glass. No one need be told that his throat is painful; he knows that already. When we have a cold, the small glands which lie within the nostrils do not work properly, and send out a large quantity of unhealthy juice. Besides all this, there is a feeling of considerable discomfort throughout the body.

Colds in the head are bad enough in themselves for the reason just mentioned; but they become serious for other reasons. When the lining of the nose and throat is irritated and swollen from a long continued cold, and children so troubled happen to go into a house where there is measles, scarlet fever, diphtheria, or small-pox, the germs may start to grow upon the red and swollen surface or they may pass through the skin and get into the blood and set up the disease.

Some people are more liable to catch cold than others. Either they are naturally weak and delicate, or they have made themselves "soft" by wearing too much clothing. People who remain much in over-heated houses in winter or who always wash the face and throat in warm or lukewarm water, are also very liable to catch cold.

We can do much to make ourselves hardy and keep ourselves free from colds, by taking a cold bath every morning, summer and winter, or at least by always washing the face, hands, neck, and chest with cold water, and rubbing vigorously afterwards with a coarse towel. But a cold bath should never be taken in a cold bathroom. Nor if one is suffering from a cold should he take a cold bath. Chilling oneself should always be avoided. Even the chilling of the hands or feet may give one a cold or make a cold grow worse.

## CHAPTER XVI

### THE TEETH

The chief cause of the decay of teeth is their not being kept clean. Little patches of food cling to the teeth after every meal, and, not being brushed off as they should be, they harbour bacteria. Very soon these patches begin to spoil, and, because the bacteria grow in the decaying food, an acid, something like vinegar, forms on the tooth and makes it begin to decay.

Some boys think it is a grand thing to be able to crack nuts with their teeth. In truth, it is very silly, because, cracking nuts in this way may break the fine, white, hard covering of a tooth, and, when once this happens, it is not very long until a cavity forms and causes toothache.

Whenever a cavity forms the only wise thing to do as soon as it is observed is to go to a dentist and have it filled. The filling not only stops the decay, but it keeps out the little bits of food that would otherwise worry the nerve and cause toothache. When properly filled the tooth may be saved for many years.

The accompanying figure shows all the principal parts of a tooth. The top part or "crown" is above the gums, but the "root" is hidden in the jaw. The crown consists of two substances, an outer covering of hard, white, shining "enamel" and inside of this a kind of bone known as "dentine." In the very middle of the dentine is a hollow containing what has been named the "pulp," and consisting of blood-vessels and a nerve.

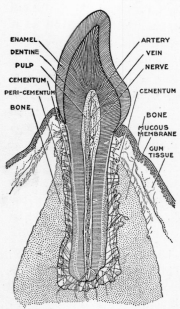

FIGURE 31.—Section of a tooth showing enamel, dentine, cement and pulp cavity.

A tooth may become so very badly decayed that it has to be pulled out, though many badly decayed or broken teeth may be made perfectly useful by having artificial crowns put on them. The loss of even one tooth is a serious matter to any person ; but, when several teeth have been removed, all because a man has been too careless to brush them or to have the cavities filled, then Nature punishes him in another way.

What further punishment do you suppose Nature inflicts?

The loss of a number of teeth makes it hard for us to chew our food as we ought. And, when we do not chew our food thoroughly; that is, when we swallow it before we have ground it into fine pieces and mixed it well with the juices of the mouth, we are very likely, after a few years, to have pains in the stomach. And so it comes to pass, in the course of time, that the pains of toothache are followed by the pains of indigestion.

To see some people eat, one would think that their teeth were of little or no use to them. They bite off a piece of food, chew it just once or twice, and then swallow it. In short, they bolt their food just as dogs do. Often they hurry the swallowing by taking great gulps of tea, coffee, or water.

Now, no wise person will do this, because bolting one's food throws too much of the work of digestion upon the stomach and brings on indigestion. All food should be thoroughly chewed. A piece of meat, for example, should be chewed twenty or thirty times, or until it has been reduced to a liquid pulp. People should eat very slowly, and they should take a certain quantity of hard food, such as nuts, crusts of bread and biscuit, in order to polish their teeth and keep the gums healthy.

Toothache, then, is one of the means by which Nature teaches us to take care of our health. When we treat our teeth badly, or our skin, or our stomach, Nature sooner or later makes us suffer pain. If we are wise, we try to find out, either by ourselves or from a doctor, what wrong we have done to our bodies, and we try to avoid doing the wrong in the future.

Some parents, knowing that their children lose all their first or " temporary " teeth between six and twelve years of age, do not think it worth while to have the first teeth cared for by a dentist. But the temporary teeth should be kept clean, and the holes in them should be filled, just the same as in the case of the second or "permanent" set of teeth. When the first ones are well cared for, the child has no toothache, it can chew its food better, the food nourishes the body better, the child grows larger and stronger, and the permanent teeth are better.

Hence good teeth help us to keep well and strong.

When we are in good health there are not so many of the invisible plants and their tiny seeds in the mouth; they do not grow so fast nor do so much harm. On the other hand, when we are weak or sick, and have a bad breath and our stomachs are out of order, the seeds grow very much faster, and make cavities in our teeth and

FIGURE 32.—Protruding teeth.

do us ever so much more harm.

When the temporary teeth are taken out too soon or are left in too long, the permanent ones grow in crooked and spoil the beauty of the mouth. The dentist remedies this defect, by using gentle pressure and keeping it applied to the teeth for months. In this way he presses the uneven teeth back into place, and often without pain.

There is another fact to be noted here. Some people are blessed in having been born strong. Just because they come into the world strong, healthy babies, they grow into strong, healthy boys and girls, and their teeth are strong, hard, white, and shining—teeth which the invisible plants can scarcely harm at all. On the other hand, there are babies who are born with weak bodies, and especially with weak bones. When they grow up to be boys and girls, they have teeth that are soft,—that crack easily and decay

FIGURE 33.—The same after adjustment by a dentist.

soon, and require a great deal of care to keep them from being lost. Many strong people, too, have sound teeth up to sixty or seventy years of age, while others lose all their teeth before they are thirty. Generally, the one class of people get their good teeth from healthy parents ; the other class get their bad teeth from delicate parents.

But, while all this is quite true, it is also true that whether we are blessed with strong, healthy teeth, or suffer from bad and decayed ones, we should wash them and brush them and try to preserve them as long as we can.

FIGURE 34.—Teeth that have become bad through a bad heredity.

[See Chapter XLI.]

As soon as a man has lost so many teeth that he cannot chew his food properly, then, if he wishes to remain in good health, he should go to a dentist and have the lost teeth replaced by artificial ones. These should be carefully brushed after every meal, and at night should be removed from the mouth and kept in a glass of water to which has been added a few drops of a solution of borax, or baking soda, or some other suitable mouth wash.

The great matter in caring for the teeth is to keep them perfectly clean. The tougher portions of food which become fixed between the teeth, should be removed with a quill or wooden toothpick, and the soft particles should be brushed off with a tooth-brush after every meal. The brushing should be done upwards and downwards, never across the teeth. In this way the white patches of food can be most easily removed. Once in a while the crown of each tooth should be polished with tooth-powder on a narrow chisel-like piece of wood. This will prevent the formation of the crust, called "tartar," which helps to make the teeth decay.

## CHAPTER XVII

### DIGESTION

Digestion starts in the mouth. "But how can it start in the mouth," you ask, "when the food remains there such a very short time?" Quite true, it does remain a very short time in the mouths of people who eat quickly; but it remains a comparatively long time in the mouths of people who care for their digestion. These latter keep the food in the mouth until it has been chewed almost into a liquid. By doing so, the saliva and the food become so thoroughly mixed that, when the liquid reaches the stomach, the saliva continues for about forty minutes to change the starches of the food into a kind of sugar. This change into sugar goes on until a good deal of the juice of the stomach—which is called the gastric juice—has been formed.

In the stomach a second stage in digestion takes place. Here the gastric juice changes the lean meats of the food into a soluble form, in somewhat the same way as saliva changes the starches into soluble sugar. Both of the foregoing changes are necessary; for, if our food always remained in the solid form in which it is eaten, the blood could get very little nourishment out of it. As a matter of fact, all digestion, whether in the mouth, the stomach, or the intestines, means the change of solid food into soluble food. Only through such a change as this can the

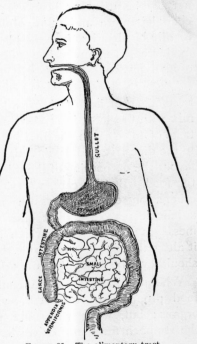

FIGURE 35.—The alimentary tract.

food pass into the intestinal walls and be carried onward in the blood to nourish all parts of the body.

In the part of the intestine immediately beyond the stomach, namely the duodenum, the food enters upon a third stage in its digestion. Here it meets with three other juices, the bile, the pancreatic juice, and the intestinal juice. The bile comes from the liver ; the pancreatic juice comes from the pancreas, a gland which lies alongside of the duodenum ; and the intestinal juice comes from the walls of the intestine. All three juices act together upon the food as it passes down the intestine, changing more and more of it into forms which will readily be absorbed into the blood. So you see that the food is acted upon by five different juices in the course of its digestion.

While the mere passage of the food along the intestine is sufficient of itself to cause all five juices to form and mix with the food, it is well known that the odour and taste of food cause the brain to send special messages to the digestive glands, and that these messages greatly favour the outpouring of the juices and their action upon the food. But let care, worry, anxiety, sorrow, or any other strong emotion press upon a person, especially upon a delicate person, and at once there start other nerve messages from the brain which hinder digestion or stop it altogether. Hence the rule that no cares or worries should ever be brought to the table during meal-time.

When the stomach and intestines are digesting the food properly, we do not know that we possess these organs ; but, when we suffer pain after eating and the stomach feels sore or tender on being touched, we may be quite sure that we have indigestion. It is unwise to neglect the plain hints which Nature thus gives us in the form of discomfort, pain, weakness, and the heavy beat of the heart, known as " palpitation."

This weakness is easily understood. If the stomach and bowels do not digest properly, the blood cannot get enough nourishment out of the food and so cannot give sufficient nourishment to the nerves and muscles. The consequence is that we feel sick and weak and cannot do our work.

There are many causes of indigestion which it would be useless to discuss in detail with you ; but, they may all be roughly summed up by saying that indigestion is due (1) to eating the wrong kinds of food, (2) to eating improperly cooked food, (3) to eating food in the wrong way, that is too fast, (4) to eating too much food, (5) to working fast or working hard soon after eating, or (6) to the fact that a person has been born with weak digestive organs.

How many of these causes can you control ? You say, of course, that, when you become men and women with homes of your own you can control all of them except the last, and you are possibly right. A boy who has come into the world with a weak stomach and intestines, is badly handicapped in the race of life. Fortunately, there are not many such children. Those who are thus afflicted must always have the special care of mothers, nurses, and doctors.

But except with the few who have delicate digestive organs, indigestion is a disease which may be avoided altogether if people will only take the necessary trouble, or exercise the necessary self-control. The first symptoms must, however, be noted ; for it is one of those diseases which come on so gradually and imperceptibly as to be upon us almost before we are aware of it.

Sometimes indigestion shews itself in the form of either constipation or diarrhœa. While the food and liquids are passing through the intestine—in all a distance of 25 or 30 feet,—it often happens that much of the liquid is withdrawn from the bowel into the blood. When this takes place, the undigested portions of the food may become hardened and then their passage out of the body becomes difficult.   This is what is meant by "constipation."   On the other hand, little or no liquid may be removed from the bowel during digestion ; in fact, more liquid may be added to what is already in the intestine, and then the discharges are very watery. This condition is known as "diarrhœa."

Now both these conditions are often due to errors in diet, and they can both, generally speaking, be cured by choosing a proper diet and persevering in its use.   In the case of diarrhœa, you may have to follow a prescribed diet for only a few days ; in the case of constipation, you may have to persevere in its use for weeks or even months. In all obstinate cases of either disease you should consult a physician.

Constipation is the source of a great deal of misery and suffering in the form of headache, tiredness, and giddiness.   No doubt some of its ill effects are due to the fact that the natural drainage of waste from the intestine becomes blocked up.   To prevent it, plenty of fruits, vegetables, vegetable soups, and salads should be eaten, but these must not be too highly seasoned.   A glass of cold water the first thing in the morning often helps, and so does deep breathing.   Then, too, a person must take plenty of exercise in the form of work or of games, and should as far as possible relieve the bowels at the same hour every day.   This last rule is very important.

The temptation to use medicines for the relief of constipation is very great ; but you will do well to avoid them. Of course, there can be no harm in taking a little laxative medicine now and again to help in overcoming an obstinate attack of constipation ; but laxatives will never produce a permanent cure. As already pointed out, diet and exercise in the fresh air are the only simple remedy for constipation.

In order to avoid diarrhœa you must refrain from eating raw vegetables, unripe fruit, over-ripe fruit, stale fish, or stale meat. In hot weather, microbes increase very rapidly in these foods, and these when eaten uncooked are a frequent cause of diarrhœa. Stale milk is particularly harmful for infants, among whom the death-rate from diarrhœa is very high, especially in July and August when milk is most likely to be bad. Boiled milk, a poached egg and toast are suitable for one suffering from diarrhœa. This diet, with perfect rest in bed or on a couch, will remedy all simple cases.

A word or two may be said here in regard to the act of eating. There should be regular hours for meals. Some children eat too fast and eat too much, and often as a consequence make themselves sick. Very little liquid should be drunk with meals, unless care is taken to chew the food as long and thoroughly as if no liquid were taken.

Another rule is not to play or do any kind of work immediately after eating. There should be a rest of half an hour after each meal to allow digestion to go on unhindered.

Next in importance to selecting plain, wholesome, fresh foods, is the duty of seeing that they are well cooked. As regards this, girls must rely upon instructions which they can get from their mothers, and from useful books upon these subjects.

---

# CHAPTER XVIII

## FOODS

Everyone knows what would happen if we took no food. We should soon die. How long we could live without eating would depend upon a number of things. If we could have plenty of water to drink and the weather were mild, we might live a week or ten days. If we were very strong and had plenty of food stored in our bodies in the form of fat, and if we could, in addition to getting water, lie in a comfortable bed, we might live for, perhaps, five or six weeks; but, sooner or later, the body would have to get nourishment from some source.

Fruit-trees, vegetables, and grains rapidly increase in strength and size when they are well fed, but they remain weak and small when ill fed. Upon many a sandy hill or gravelly knoll the grass is scanty and short because it is ill fed, whereas on rich, moist flats it is long and thick. Animals, too, grow strong and fat when they get plenty of nourishing food. This statement is easily verified by observing the young cattle upon any first-class farm.

This is a general law in the growth of all living things: herbs, trees, grasses, fowl, cattle, sheep, horses, and human beings, all vary in vigour and health—being large and strong, or thin and sickly—according as they get plenty of food, or too little.

What is the best kind of food for human beings? That will depend upon a number of things, but chiefly upon the age, occupation, and climate. In a small book like this, it will not be possible to explain how the kind and quantity of food should be varied to suit young people and old people, or to suit those who live sedentary lives as compared with those who live very active lives. Much less will it be possible to explain why the Icelanders eat large quantities of fat, and the Fiji Islanders eat chiefly fruits and vegetables. Rather let me point out, first of all, what kinds of food are essential to health, and explain afterwards as clearly as possible how much of each kind should be eaten in order to be well and strong.

It has been found by experience that pure rich milk is the best article of food that we know of for persons in normal health. Moreover, in a wasting disease like consumption, which is so called because it is a disease in which the body grows thinner and lighter all the time, the two foods upon which a patient is almost invariably fed are milk and raw eggs? In most cases these foods have been found to be the most easily digested and the most nourishing.

What does milk consist of? Chemists who have analyzed it tell us that the milk from a healthy cow contains the five following substances :—

|  |  | PARTS |
|---|---|---|
| I | Proteid or curdy matter.....................about | $3\frac{1}{2}$ |
| II | Fat, that is, the cream or butter .............. " | $3\frac{1}{2}$ |
| III | The carbohydrate, milk sugar................. " | 5 |
| IV | Salts, like table salt......................... " | $\frac{3}{4}$ |
| V | Water ...................................... " | 87 |

Total 100

These are the substances found in milk, and these substances or others very like them must be taken into the body as food. Moreover, the proportions in which they occur in milk are just about the proper proportions in which we should take them in all our other foods. Of course these proportions vary with different people. Some can eat but very little proteid without becoming ill; some can eat much more and be benefited by it. The same thing is true of fats, and to a less extent of starches and sugars. It is impossible, therefore, to tell the exact amount that will suit everybody. All that can be done is to give the average diet of a number of people.

One thing is certain, the selection cannot be left to the sense of taste, at any rate in the case of children and others who have no self-control, because they would soon make themselves ill by a wrong diet. An excess of sugars, preserved fruits, and probably pastry, would be eaten, and dyspepsia and finally indigestion would be the result.

Ranke, a German scientist, has studied the selection of foods, and thinks that the following are about the right quantities for a full-grown man to eat each day, women on the average eating somewhat less :—

| | |
|---|---|
| Proteids or curdy matter.......... | 2 to 3½ oz. |
| Fats........................... | 3     " |
| Carbohydrates (sugar and starch) .. | 9 to 12   " |
| Water, tea, coffee, up to about..... | 85  fluid  " |

Salt, in addition to what is in the food, is usually taken in quantity to suit the taste.

Next to milk, perhaps the best food for young people and sickly people is eggs ; for eggs contain the same

five things that milk does, and in about the right
amounts to make good blood. The white of the egg is
much the same as the curds of milk, and the yolk contains some fat like cream, some sugar like the milk
sugar, and some salt. And, of course, there is a good
deal of water in an egg, just as there is in milk.

That eggs make the very best of flesh and blood, is
clear from the fact that the white and yolk of the egg
turn into flesh, bones, muscles, nerves, stomach, and liver
of the chick during the three weeks in which the hen is
hatching out her chickens. We must not wonder then,
if a somewhat similar change takes place in our bodies
when we eat eggs. The white and the yolk, making up
the five things which must be present in all good food,
turn into blood, and the blood repairs the waste in our
bodies and keeps us alive and well.

Bread is perhaps a commoner article of food for
grown-up people than milk or eggs. Are these same
five things present in it? Yes, they are, but not in the
right proportions. Wheat, from which white bread is
made, contains about 12 parts of what may be called
the curds of wheat; about 1½ parts of what we may
call the fat; about 70 parts of starch, a substance that
is a sort of first cousin to sugar; about 14½ parts of
water; and 2 parts of salt.

If we had to live on bread and water, which was the
only food that jailers used to give to prisoners long ago,
we should have to eat a great deal more bread than we
need in order to get the right quantity of curdy
matter for the blood. In doing this we should take a
great deal more starchy matter than is good for the
blood. So that, in taking the right amount of curdy

matter, we should be taking the wrong amount of starchy matter. Now, while this would certainly not kill us, it would not be good for us. After some time we should probably become ill and have to go to a doctor.

I knew a mother once, and she was a very fond mother too, who did a good deal of harm to her own health and to that of her three children, because she did not understand these facts about food. Of course she ate bread ; also porridge made from different kinds of grain, such as oats, wheat, and corn. Her children had learned to like these foods, and ate them with syrup, not merely at breakfast but often at supper as well. Puddings made of wheat-flour, cornstarch, or rice were often taken at dinner. The sugar or syrup which was eaten with the puddings or porridge helped to make them tasty, and therefore the children did not object to eating them often. But in the course of a few years, the mother's health began to fail. For one thing, she lost weight ; she became pale and weak ; her heart beat much faster than it should ; and she grew nervous and worried about everything. Her husband, seeing that she was ill, induced her to consult a doctor.

At first the doctor was a little puzzled, because he could find no trace of disease about her. On learning what her diet was, he discovered what was wrong. She had not been taking enough curdy matter in her food ; in short she was slowly starving herself, though all the while she was eating plenty of starchy food. As her husband was not able to buy meat or fowl, the doctor advised her to eat plenty of cheese. Cheese, as you know, is made up chiefly of the curds and fat of milk, and these two things made up almost exactly what had been lacking in her diet. As a result, she gradually improved in health and strength.

Instead of telling his patient to eat cheese with her starchy foods, the doctor might have advised good fat beef. Would this make up for what is lacking in bread and porridge? Let us see. If we analyzed beef as we did milk, we should find that the lean meat makes up about 17 parts of curdy matter; that the fat is almost exactly like butter or the fat of milk, and amounts to about 26 parts. Beef contains also a mere trace of starch or sugar, 4 parts of salt, and the rest, about 53 parts, consists of water. So we see that fat beef would have helped the patient quite as well as cheese.

Now, if we tried to live on beefsteak and water, we should become ill after a time. We could live for years on bread, beefsteak, salt, and water; but not on bread, salt, and water; nor on beefsteak, salt, and water. The trouble is that bread and porridge do not contain enough curdy matter and fat, and that beefsteak has too much curdy matter and not enough of the sugar or starchy matter. But bread and meat together furnish just about the right amounts of curd, fat, and starch, for making good blood.

How about potatoes? Do they contain the five things necessary for the support of life? Yes, but not in the proper proportions. They contain a very little curd— 2 parts out of a hundred—which is not enough to make good blood. They contain about 75 parts of water; a great deal of starch, 20 parts, which we have called the first cousin to sugar; a little salt, 3 parts; and a mere trace of fat, $\frac{1}{10}$ of 1 part. In fact, potatoes alone would be poor food for grown-up people, and very poor food indeed for growing boys and girls. No doubt, a man might live a long time on potatoes, salt, and water ; but in time, long or short, depending upon his strength, he would come to feel ill, and would lose his strength.

The drawback about potatoes is that they do not contain enough vegetable curd for the blood, and they contain, in proportion, too much starch. A man who eats potatoes alone or beefsteak alone, always feels hungry. He may eat large quantities of either one of them, but his hunger is not satisfied. He may not know that his blood is craving for more curdy matter, when he has eaten a large quantity of potatoes. Nor may he know that his blood is craving for more starchy matter, when he has already eaten a large quantity of beefsteak. But he may readily observe that, when he eats potatoes and beefsteak together, a much less quantity of each satisfies his hunger.

---

# CHAPTER XIX

## DIET

We have seen that fat alone, or starch alone, or its first cousin sugar alone, will not make blood. Nor will these three together make blood. Curd is absolutely necessary. It does not require much curd to support life, but some curd we must have. We may get the curd from milk, from eggs, from meat, or we may get it from vegetables like peas or beans, which contain a great deal of vegetable curd—a good deal more than bread does—but, we must get a certain amount of it from some source. And in the same way, we must get a certain amount of fat ;

not too much, and not too little, but just enough for the needs of the body. So, too, in the case of starch or sugar; a certain amount of this is necessary for making healthy blood.

As I said before, it is very hard to tell exactly how much of each of the three real foods—proteids, fats, and carbohydrates—is necessary for health. The amount varies in different persons, and it varies also in the same person from time to time.

I know a geologist, that is, a man who studies rocks. During the summer he was out in the fields or in the woods, walking miles and miles every day. He chipped off pieces of rock here and there and came back to his camp every night pretty well tired out, with a bag full of stones on his back. This hard work he kept up for months. In late autumn, when the snow fell, and he could do field work no longer, he went into an office in a city and studied the pieces of rock which he had gathered during the summer.

Now this winter work was very different from that of the summer. In the office he had little or no exercise— his muscles and nerves did very little work. But, as he usually returned to the city with a good appetite, he ate just as much as when he was out in camp. The blood sucked up most of the good of the food; but, as the muscles and nerves were not being exercised, they did not need so much nourishment, and so the blood could not get rid of all the nourishment which it had obtained from the food. The consequence was that the extra nourishment went round and round the body from head to foot, doing no good,—in fact doing harm.

So at last one winter the geologist became ill. He had headache and was dizzy and had pains in his stomach and liver. Being a thoughtful fellow, he soon suspected what was wrong. He reduced the amount of his food, took more exercise, and was soon all right again.

I have known young men who have been working hard upon the farm, fall sick in a similar way when they have given up this outdoor labour and gone to school or college. Such a sudden change is likely to bring on ill health. It should take place gradually. Care should be taken to avoid the danger by lessening the amount of food consumed, and by taking vigorous exercise either in the form of long walks, or in football, hockey, or gymnastic exercises.

In the summer we should eat more fruits and vegetables ; in the winter, more curdy matter and fats. Nansen, the famous Arctic explorer, tells us that he and his men used to get up in the middle of the night to eat fats or drink oil. They had a strong craving for this kind of food. It was needed by the body in order to make heat. The great cold of the north made them eat large quantities of fat, which they would have loathed when in their southern homes.

The question of diet brings up another very important matter. In 1889, the Commissioner of Education in Washington published some very important statements about the pupils in the Washington schools. These facts are almost exactly like some other facts which have been published regarding pupils in some European schools. Remember that these statements are based upon the average of a large number of measurements of boys and girls. There must, therefore, be children who are exceptions to the general rules here laid down; for example, some big-headed boys learn slowly, while some small-headed boys are very bright and quick in their studies. But apart from such exceptions, the general statements hold good. These are as follows :—

1. As the circumference of head increases, ability increases.

2. The children of intelligent people have a larger circumference of head than the children of the ignorant.

3. Bright boys are taller and heavier than dull boys.

4. Children of intelligent people have greater height, weight, and length of body than children of the ignorant.

5. Children of intelligent people show greater ability in their studies than children of the ignorant.

These facts seem to mean that the children who are best fed, best clothed, and best housed, will, as a rule, have the best chance to get on in the world; whereas, poorly fed, ill clad, and poorly housed children can hardly ever hope to be more than hewers of wood and drawers of water for others. Poorly fed children are those who get too little milk, too few eggs, and too little butter and meat, because these kinds of food cost much more money than vegetable foods do.

Poor people cannot afford to buy high-priced foods, and must therefore content themselves with feeding their children upon bread and starchy vegetables, and sometimes they cannot buy enough even of these. What happens to such children?

Suppose a mother can afford to feed her children only on bread and potatoes. They cannot get enough nourishment out of these foodstuffs. Large quantities may be eaten and yet the children will be hungry. The foodstuffs do not contain enough curdy matter for the blood, and, without the mother's knowing it, she is actually starving her children. Of course, the children

FIGURE 36.—Three children of the same age. The difference in size is not due to difference in diet.

are getting all the vegetable food that they can eat, but the trouble is that there is not enough nourishment in this kind of food to make children grow strong and healthy.

Again, there are parents who do not know how to feed their children. They think that so long as there is *plenty* to eat, their children are being well provided for; whereas a great deal of harm may be done to them. It is just as important to have the right kind of food as it is to have plenty of it; because, if it is not of the right kind, it will not have the proper substances in it or it will not digest properly, and the blood will not be able to get enough nourishment out of it.

Expensive pies, puddings, cakes, jam, and confectionery may contain very little more nourishment than bread and potatoes. The whole question is not one of cost merely; it is one of selection as well. In fact, poor parents who are, nevertheless, willing to study the diet of children and to acquire some skill in cookery may in the end bring up stronger and healthier children than the rich.

Bunge, a German chemist, gives the following as the composition of different kinds of foodstuffs. In every case the figures mean parts in a hundred :—

| Foodstuff. | Proteid. | Fat. | Carbohydrates. |
|---|---|---|---|
| Apples | $\frac{2}{5}$ | — | 13 |
| Carrots | $1\frac{1}{10}$ | $\frac{1}{5}$ | 9 |
| Potatoes | 2 | $\frac{1}{10}$ | 20 |
| Human Milk | 2 | 4 | 6 |
| Cabbages | $3\frac{1}{3}$ | $\frac{7}{10}$ | 7 |
| Cow's Milk | $3\frac{2}{5}$ | 4 | 5 |
| Rice | 8 | $\frac{9}{10}$ | 77 |
| Corn | 10 | $4\frac{3}{5}$ | 71 |
| Wheat | 12 | $1\frac{7}{10}$ | 70 |
| White of Eggs | 13 | $\frac{3}{10}$ | — |
| Yolk of Eggs | 16 | 32 | — |
| Fat Pork | 15 | 37 | — |
| Fat Beef | 17 | 26 | — |
| Fish (pike) | 18 | $\frac{1}{2}$ | — |
| Lean Beef | 21 | $1\frac{1}{2}$ | — |
| Peas | 23 | $1\frac{4}{5}$ | 58 |

Underfed and ill fed children cannot grow so large nor be so strong as they ought to be, and they will thus be handicapped during their whole lives. They will not possess the ability which better fed children have; they will not be able to get so good an education, nor will they possess the same power of doing hard work; and therefore they will not get on so well when they become men and women.

While I have been urging that children should be well fed in order to become strong men and women, I would say also that there is a prior condition necessary in children if they are to grow into big, sturdy adults. They must be born of strong fathers and mothers. As a rule, strong parents have strong children, and sickly parents have delicate children. Sometimes, however, it happens that a puny child is born to sturdy parents, and a fairly strong child to weakling parents.

It only remains to say a few words about the quality of foods. All food should be fresh, clean, and of the best quality. If not kept absolutely clean, it cannot remain fresh; because even the least trace of dust and bacteria upon fruits, vegetables, meat, or milk, starts decay. The growth of bacteria is slower upon fruits and vegetables than upon milk and meat; but their presence on any and all kinds of food is soon followed by a measure of decay, and even slightly decayed food is unwholesome.

How shall we manage to keep our food fresh? There is not much difficulty in winter. Frost delays or stops the growth of bacteria, and decay therefore comes to a stand-still; but, in warm weather, recourse must be had to the ice-box. While a good refrigerator is an absolute necessity in keeping food free from staleness and decay, it must not be forgotten that an unclean refrigerator may become little better than a pest-box. In order to be healthful it should be kept scrupulously clean.

## CHAPTER XX

### SALTS, TEA, AND COFFEE

We have seen that milk, eggs, bread, and meat all contain two other kinds of food besides the curds, fat, and starch. They contain water and certain other substances which by learned men are called salts. Are the salts of any use? Yes, a great deal. We cannot live without these salts any more than we can live without the curd. Of course, everyone knows that we eat table salt with the food; but the other salts which we take into the body with our food, are quite as essential for health as table salt.

These other salts when extracted by chemists look like table salt, but are different from it. They are found in most fruits and vegetables. In fact, we eat certain vegetables raw, such as onions, lettuce, and celery, largely on account of these other salts which are in them. When we eat these vegetables raw, we get the good of all the salts that they contain. When they are boiled, the boiling takes out a great deal of the salts; and, if the water in which they are boiled is thrown away, we lose the good of the salts. But, when vegetables are used in making soup, these salts are all kept in the soup; and this is one reason why soups are so good for us.

How do we know that salts are necessary? In a very simple way. When dogs are fed on food which has no salt of any kind in it, they sicken and die in about a month. You may feed them as much curd, fat, and starch as you like, but without salts in their food these animals cannot live. And exactly the same thing would happen to us if we tried to live without salts.

No one knows precisely what the salts do for us when we take them into the body. We do know that they help to turn the curds into a liquid. You can see this for yourself any time, by putting the white and yolk of a slightly hard-boiled egg into a tumbler, adding about a quarter of a teaspoonful of salt and stirring it briskly with a spoon. You will soon see that some of the hard pieces get soft, and give rise to a yellowish liquid.

You know that sugar disappears when it is stirred up in water. We say that the sugar has "gone into solution" in the water. So the table salt puts a little of the egg into solution. And, in somewhat the same way, the salts which we eat, help to keep the curdy matter of the food in solution in the juices of the mouth and stomach and bowels and in the blood.

There are other uses which you cannot understand; but the important thing to know is that we must have certain salts as part of our food. They seem to act like oil on a piece of machinery; indeed, we may say that they keep the machinery of our bodies in good working order.

Water, too, is just as necessary as the other four kinds of food. You cannot live on dry food. If you try to eat dry bread, you will find that you can eat some of it, but not much. After a little while, you find yourself choking and must drink a little water or some other liquid.

People can live longer without the other kinds of food than they can without water.  Water does not itself give us any strength : but, along with the salts, it keeps the curds and fats and starches in solution, so that the blood can suck the good out of them as they pass down the intestine.  As water makes up about nine-tenths of the blood, the water may be said to be the means by which our food is withdrawn from the bowels and carried all over the body to the flesh and muscles and nerves, and other parts which need to be nourished.

Water, then, is part of our food just as much as curd or salt is.  We must take a certain amount of it every day, if the other foodstuffs do not contain enough water. If we use much milk, we need not take any water. But if we use bread and butter and cheese, or other such foods, we need to drink a great deal of water. Here, however, the same rule holds good as in the case of other foods : we must take neither too little water nor too much.  But it would not be quite so bad for us to take too much or too little water as it would be to take too much or too little curd.

Too much of any of the foods is bad for us.  Too much of any one of them—even water—would sicken us, because everything which we eat and which our bodies do not need, will do us harm.  They go round and round in the blood and act as a kind of poison.

But besides the five things which are absolutely necessary for us as food, there are some other things which many people take, which they have learned to like, and which they say do them no harm.  I mean tea, coffee, cocoa, and wine, beer, and a number of other drinks containing alcohol, or spirits of wine.  What about these?

Are they necessary, like the foods, or can we live without them?

There is no doubt as to what the answer should be. They are certainly not necessary to keep us well and strong. Much less are they necessary to keep us alive. Foods we must have, including liquids of some kind; but tea, coffee, and all kinds of drinks containing spirits of wine, or alcohol, need not be taken at all. Many people never take any of these drinks, and they feel none the worse. On the other hand, it must be said that many people who have drunk tea, coffee, and cocoa daily for years, maintain that they have not been harmed by them.

Tea and coffee are not drunk because they are real foods. The only real foods in a cup of tea or coffee are the milk and sugar. Tea and coffee are drunk at meals or between meals, because they freshen us up a little, and enable us do things which we might not be able to do if we did not drink them. They do not nourish the body, as curds, fats, and sugars or starches do; they simply act somewhat like the salts of the food; they oil the machinery of our body and make it work more quickly. They do not give any real strength. They whip up the working of the body and make it pay out its strength more quickly than it otherwise would; but they cannot take the place of any of the real foods.

Some people think that these drinks help them to work, just as well as milk does; but such is not the case. People who eat bread and butter, and drink two or three cups of tea or coffee feel better and stronger than if they took milk; but the strength comes entirely from the bread and butter and the milk and sugar. Indeed, in this case, tea and coffee only force the body to use up the real foods so much the more quickly. A man cannot work long on a diet of bread, butter, and tea. His strength will soon give out; it is false strength. Nothing can give true strength but the real foods.

Is there no place, then, for tea and coffee in a wholesome diet? Yes, there is; but it is doubtful if there is any useful place for these drinks in the diet of young people.

The machinery of a boy's body, as a rule, works better without tea or coffee. If he is in good health, his nerves and muscles do not need to be whipped up to make them work any faster. They work well enough of their own accord. Perhaps, if boys or girls are out of sorts a little, and not feeling very well, a cup of tea or coffee will do them no harm and may do them some good; but, as a general thing, no young person needs the spur of a cup of tea to make his body do good work. A cup of warm milk would do him far more good than tea or coffee.

It is different with grown-up people, and certainly with people in middle life. Tea and coffee often do such people good, especially if they do not feel so well as usual. Suppose they have eaten enough of the real foods but are nevertheless feeling a little unfit for their work, then a cup of tea or coffee will make them feel better.

If you *will* drink tea, then you should learn how to make it so that when you drink it, it will do you the least harm. By pouring hot water on the tea-leaves and allowing the mixture to stand for about five minutes, you will get all the pleasant stuff—all the refreshing part—out of the tea. But, if you boil tea-leaves for fifteen minutes or half an hour, as I have often seen cooks do in a lumber camp, you take out of the tea-leaves, not merely the refreshing stuff but other stuff besides, and then the tea tastes bitter and unpleasant.

This other stuff, which may be boiled out of the leaves, is found in other plants besides the tea plant. It is found in the bark of the oak and the hemlock, and tanners use it in tanning hides, that is, for turning the skin of the ox into leather. Now, you know how hard leather is. It has been made hard by steeping the soft skins of oxen and other animals in oak bark and water, or hemlock bark and water.

Instead of using oak or hemlock, a tanner might use a liquid made by boiling tea-leaves in water. This also would harden soft hides, but it would be a costly way of tanning. A partial effect of this nature is what takes place in the stomachs of people who are in the habit of drinking much tea that has been kept hot for a long time on the stove. Not that the tea could ever actually turn the coats of the stomach into leather, but tea that has been boiled for a long time does injure the stomach and bring on indigestion.

If any of you doubt that tea and coffee whip up the working of the body and excite the nerves, you have only to try the effect of drinking two or three cups of either of them at bed-time. Unless you have very strong nerves, you will find that you can not go to sleep at your usual hour. You will lie awake, perhaps, for two or three hours, and will turn from side to side, thinking about many things. In the morning you may have a headache, and you will feel tired and out of sorts.

In short, strong tea and coffee throw your body out of good working order, and though their use has none of the degrading effects of alcohol or opium, yet young people do not need them and should avoid their use.   Young people need to store up strength—not to spend it quickly.

## CHAPTER XXI

### THE BLOOD AND THE LYMPH

No one needs to be told what blood looks like.   If a cut in the flesh is large and deep, the blood comes out here and there in jets from a set of tubes, called "arteries." At the same time and from the same cut the blood may well up from another set of tubes called " veins," as water does from a spring.

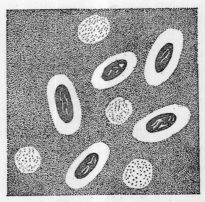

Very soon after the cut has been made, some of the blood forms a jelly-like mass called a "clot," which adheres

FIGURE 37.—The oval figures with dark centres represent the red blood corpuscles in a frog's blood.   These carry oxygen from the lungs all over the body.   The round dotted figures represent the white blood corpuscles.   These help to carry food materials to the tissues.

to the surface of the wound.   The use of the clot is to stop bleeding.   Loss of blood is so very serious that Nature has been careful to make the blood of all animals clot very soon after it leaves the blood-vessels.

Freshly shed blood is composed of a pale straw-coloured liquid called "plasma," and floating in this, a large number of very minute rounded bodies known as blood "corpuscles," or blood "cells." Of these corpuscles, there are two kinds—red ones and white ones. The white corpuscles and the plasma are the great carriers of nutritive material. The red take oxygen from the air of the lungs and carry it away in the arteries. On reaching the very smallest blood-vessels the red corpuscles deliver the oxygen to the flesh. Here the wet burning occurs about which you have already read.

About 90 per cent. of the plasma is water, and, of the rest, over 9 per cent. is nutritive material which has come from the food. The remainder—a very small part—is waste matter which has been gathered up in the course of the circulation.

The arteries carry the blood all over the body, branching and rebranching the farther away they get from the heart, and becoming smaller in diameter all the time until finally they become the fine set of tubes known as "capillaries." These convey the blood through every organ and tissue of the body.

The veins gather up the blood from the capillaries and return it to the heart again.

The arterial blood of the body is bright-red in colour, whereas the venous blood is dark-red, the change from bright-red to dark-red taking place while the blood is passing through the capillaries of the body. The change is due to the fact that the blood while in the tissues loses much of its oxygen and takes on a load of carbon dioxide. You will remember that this gas forms as a result of the burning of the body. The reverse change in colour takes place in the capillaries of the lungs. Here the venous blood changes from dark-red to bright-red through losing its carbon dioxide and taking in a fresh supply of oxygen.

The statement, therefore, that the arteries contain bright-red blood, and the veins, dark-red blood, is not true of the blood which passes from the heart to the lungs in the pulmonary artery. In this case the artery and its branches contain the dark-red blood which has come from the body tissues and is on its way to the lungs to be purified; and the veins from the lungs to the heart contain bright-red blood.

The blood in the capillaries gives the flesh its red colour, as it does also to the meat we see in every butcher's shop. Although the animal from which the lean meat comes was bled to death, yet when such meat is cut up into small pieces, soaked and squeezed for a long time in warm water, it becomes almost white.

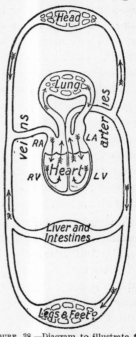

FIGURE 38.—Diagram to illustrate the pulmonary circulation, that is, the circulation through the lungs; also the systemic circulation, or that through the rest of the body. The arrows show the course which the blood takes. RA, right auricle; RV, right ventricle; LA, left auricle; LV, left ventricle. The tricuspid and the mitral valves are indicated in this figure, but not the semi-lunar valves.

The fact is that when an animal is slaughtered for market, not nearly all its blood escapes from the capillaries. Much of it remains in the flesh and gives it a reddish colour, just as the blood gives our fingers their pinkish colour.

The capillaries have very thin walls—thinner than any tissue paper—and thus allow the liquid part of the blood and the material which is dissolved in it to ooze through their walls. Some white blood corpuscles also pass out with the plasma. The plasma and corpuscles which thus escape through the capillary walls into the surrounding flesh and bone are known as "lymph."

Blood, in a healthy body, is always found inside of the blood-vessels; whereas lymph is always found outside of the blood-vessels and bathing the tissues. All lymph comes from the blood and returns to the blood again, either through the capillary walls, or by means of a special set of lymph vessels which very much resemble veins and which empty into veins near the neck

A stream of liquid nutritive material passes all the time from the blood through the capillary walls into the lymph, and from the lymph into the tissues. This nutritive material is used up in nourishing the tissues. On the other hand, there is a stream of waste material passing from the tissues into the lymph and from the lymph back again into the blood.

Lymph circulates through parts of the body where blood does not go. For example, we find no blood in the denser parts of bone, cartilage, or tendon, nor in the minute parts of muscle or nerve. Nor can we see any red blood-vessels in the white of the eye when it is perfectly healthy. But if the white of the eye gets injured you soon see faint red lines running across it, revealing the fact that blood is now circulating through minute vessels which in health contain only colourless lymph.

Whenever, therefore, you think of the work of the blood, you should also think of its sister-fluid, lymph, and try to realize that blood does not nourish any tissue directly, but only through the medium of the lymph.

Blood and lymph have two great kinds of work to perform.  In the first place they absorb from the walls of the stomach and intestines and carry to all parts of the body most of the nourishing material of the food after it has been digested ; and in the second place, they gather up from every part of the body the worn out matter of the muscles, nerves, and other kinds of flesh, and carry it to the skin, lungs, kidneys, and intestines. When the blood reaches these four organs, bearing its load of waste matter, these organs remove the waste from the blood ; that is, they purify the blood : the waste matter is then thrust out of the body.

Keeping in mind, therefore, the two great kinds of work which are done by the blood, it becomes a matter of vast importance to us to know what kind of food to eat, and how to eat it in order to make good blood ; and it becomes equally important to know how to take care of the lungs, skin, kidneys, and intestines, so that they may be able to keep the blood pure.  The healthier and more active these organs are, the more efficiently they do their work.

You have already learned how the sweat-glands take dead waste from the blood and empty it out through the pores of the skin, and how the lungs exhale other waste matter in the form of carbon dioxide and vapour of water.  The kidneys, too, are particularly important organs in purifying the blood.  In fact, the purest blood in the body is that which has just passed through these organs. By means of the kidneys, waste is excreted from the blood, that is not thrown off at all by the other three organs, or, at least, is thrown off in exceedingly small quantities. If the kidneys should stop their work of purifying blood, we could live but a short time.

## CHAPTER XXII

### CIRCULATION OF THE BLOOD

The blood is made to circulate through the body chiefly by the action of the heart. This organ is about the size of one's fist, and is composed chiefly of muscle. It contains four chambers, or cavities, the two upper ones being known as auricles, and the two lower ones as ventricles.

You have all felt your hearts beat. What is meant by a heart beat? Just this ; the heart contracts, that is, grows smaller, and presses upon the blood which fills its four chambers. As a result the blood is forced out of the two auricles into the two ventricles, and then from the two ventricles into the arteries, and is conveyed away by these tubes and their branches all over the body.

While the contraction of the heart is the main force in causing the circulation of the blood, the heart is assisted in its work by the act of breathing and by the contraction of the muscles all over the body. Vigorous exercise therefore, whether in the form of play or work, improves the circulation ; whereas sitting still or lying down hinders it.

The rate at which the blood flows is not the same in arteries, capillaries, and veins. In a large artery like the carotid in a man's neck, which carries blood from the heart to the head, the rate of flow varies from ten to

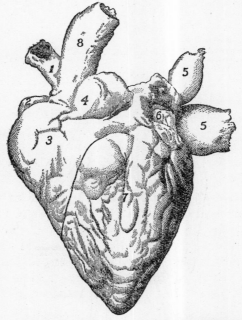

FIGURE 39.—A Sheep's Heart. 1, a vein which empties blood into 2, the right auricle. From 2 the blood passes into 3, the right ventricle; thence it passes into 4, an artery which conveys it to the lungs. From the lungs the blood returns again through the veins to 5, 5 to the left auricle 6; thence it passes into the left ventricle 7, and from this cavity it is forced into the aorta 8, and distributed all over the body.

eighteen inches per second; while, in the jugular vein which carries the blood back from the head, the rate is only about half as fast. In the capillaries the flow is exceedingly slow. This allows time for the nutritive materials to pass out through the very thin walls of the capillaries into the flesh, as well as for some of the waste material to pass from the flesh back into the capillaries.

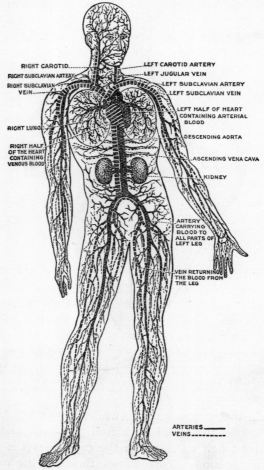

FIGURE 40.—Diagram of the circulation of the blood.

The quantity of blood passing through the different organs of the body is varying all the time. After a meal, that is, during the digestion of food, more blood goes to the stomach, intestines, and liver, than when no digestion is going on. For a similar reason, during manual labour or during great muscular exertion such as running, more blood goes to the muscles than when they are at rest. In hot weather, more blood goes to the capillaries of the skin, and, in cold weather, less blood. Generally speaking, the quantity of blood which goes to any organ varies with the amount of work which the organ has to do.

How then is the flow of blood to different parts of the body regulated? The quantity of blood going to any organ is regulated in two ways:— first, by changes in the heart-beat; secondly, by changes in the bore, or calibre, of the artery which carries blood to the organ. Both of these changes are under the control of the nervous system.

If for any reason the heart-beats become faster and stronger than usual, then the general circulation will be quickened and more blood will be sent to all the organs of the body. An opposite effect will be produced if the heart-beats become slower and feebler. The heart, in this respect, acts precisely like a pump. If the handle of a pump is worked quickly and forcibly, more water flows away from the pump spout; whereas, if the handle is worked slowly and feebly, less water flows away. In the same way, increase or decrease in the force and frequency of the heart-beat alters the quantity of blood going to every part of the body.

Every pulse-beat, such as can be felt at the wrist or on the temple, marks a beat of the heart. When a doctor, therefore, counts the pulse-beats, he is in reality counting the heart-beats.

But the quantity of blood which goes to any organ is regulated in another way. Nerve messages going to the little muscles in the walls of the arteries make them grow larger or smaller in diameter, from time to time, and consequently more blood or less blood is allowed to pass to various organs in the body, according to their varying needs. For example, while we are chewing the food, the arteries which supply the salivary glands grow larger, and allow more blood to pass to these organs. This greater blood supply enables them to make more saliva for the digestion of the food. In the same way, during digestion, the arteries which supply blood to the stomach and intestines become larger in their bore and allow more blood to pass to these organs.

And here comes in a rule of health which everyone should obey: we should never undertake any severe muscular exertion or hard study immediately after a meal. A little thought will make clear the reason for this rule. During digestion, as we have seen above, the stomach, liver, and intestines all require an increased blood supply, and they should get the increased supply by drawing it from other parts of the body. But, if we run or labour violently or study hard after eating, the working muscles or the brain, as the case may be, make a demand for more blood, and, as a consequence, neither the muscles, nor the brain, nor the digestive organs can get the increased blood supply which they require for the work that is put upon them. Under these circumstances, it is usually the digestive organs that suffer; and if the error is persisted in, indigestion results.

Besides these natural ways of regulating the flow of the blood by the nervous system, there are artificial means by which we can increase the velocity of the blood-flow throughout the body. The artificial means of influencing the blood supply are of very great importance to delicate people and to those who are suffering from any lingering disease; because a more rapid blood-flow will mean that more nutritive material will be carried to an organ and more of the waste material will be carried away from it.

Now there are two artificial ways of quickening the blood-stream; one is by giving medicines called "stimulants," which whip up the heart muscle and make it work harder or faster; the other way is by "massage." Heart stimulants, like digitalis or strychnine, should never be given except under the direction of a physician, because though they first whip up the heart, an opposite effect comes on soon afterwards and the heart-beat becomes weaker than it was before.

But stimulating the circulation by massage is a very different thing. Massage consists in kneading, pinching, rubbing, and slapping the skin and flesh all over the body in such a way as to bring the blood to the surface and promote its flow toward the heart; that is to say, the kneading and rubbing and stroking should be so directed as to aid the return to the heart of the blood from the arms, legs, and trunk.

The blood-flow being thus increased throughout the whole body, not merely are the healing processes promoted, but there is a more rapid removal of waste. Moreover, the heart is rested to some extent, because there is now no need for it to beat so fast, and consequently we find that immediately after massage the heart-beats fall some ten or a dozen per minute.

In carrying out massage, four different movements are performed :—

1. The surface to be massaged is first stroked gently in order to increase the circulation and prepare the part for the more vigorous action that follows.

2. The next movement is friction, the pressure being more firmly applied so as to influence the deeper blood-vessels.

3. The third movement is the most vigorous of all. It includes deep kneading of the part, the skin being made to rub the underlying muscles, and the veins being squeezed between the hands and the bone so as to make the blood and lymph of the arms, legs, and trunk move toward the heart.

4. Then follows a rapid tapping of the parts by means of the tips of the fingers. This again is followed by the first or stroking movement, the design being to equalize the blood-flow through the tissues which lie near the surface.

The value of massage is undoubted; but in order to be able to practise it as a calling in life, a person must take a course of instruction from a physician.

## CHAPTER XXIII

### THE STORING OF FOOD AND THE MAKING OF WHISKY

After a potato is planted it either decays entirely or else becomes smaller and smaller, and gradually dwindles to a blackish, shrunken ball, very unlike what it was at first. In the same way, the big root of the parsnip or beet shrivels up during the second year of its growth and becomes much smaller than it was at the end of the first season

FIGURE 41.—Parsnip root during the first season of growth.

Now, the substances which make up the mass of the potato and of the parsnip root must have come from their food. These plants derive part of their food from the soil in the form of water and earthy salts dissolved in the water, and they get the rest from the air, chiefly the gas, carbon dioxide, which we and other animals pass out from the lungs. These materials are digested in the green leaves when the sun is shining, and are changed into sap, and from this the material is derived which we find stored in the root, stems, leaves, or seeds of some plants.

Starch is one of the most important substances which green plants manufacture. This they store away for their own use, or for that of their offspring. Most of our foods—bread, porridge, potatoes, vegetables, and fruits come more or less directly from plants. From

plants we get the starches, sugars, oils, and salts upon which millions of human beings live. Of course, plants do not store for the use of the human race; man has simply taken possession of what plants have stored for themselves or for their off-spring.

If you examine a grain of wheat or barley you see that it is made up of two parts, a tiny baby-plant which is packed away in one corner of the seed, and surrounding the baby-plant a greater or less

FIGURE 42.—Parsnip root towards the end of the second season of growth. Compare with Figure 41.

amount of stored food in the form of curdy matter and starch. The parent plant has stored up these foods for the young plant until such time as it has grown its own roots and leaves, and can obtain food for itself from the soil and the air.

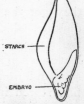

Many animals store food for their young in very much the same way as plants do. A hen's egg consists of a very tiny baby-chick lying between the white and the yolk of the egg. And the mass of white and yolk is in reality a store of food for the young chick until it is ready to leave the egg.

FIGURE 43. — Barley grain, showing the starch, and the embryo or young plant.

Often animals store food for themselves.  Squirrels, beavers, and bees lay up a store in the shape of nuts or bark or honey, for winter use.  And, in the same way, some plants, such as the beet, parsnip, and potato, store up food in the root or the stem for next season's

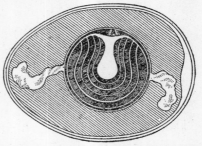

FIGURE 44.—Parts of a Hen's egg.  The dark part on top of the yolk at A represents the tiny chick.

growth ; that is, for the production of seed.

A most striking instance of storing in leaves is furnished by the soldanella, a plant which grows upon

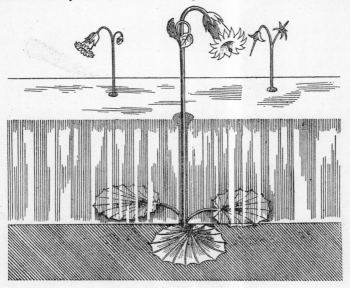

FIGURE 45.—Soldanella leaves, stem, and flower.

the Alps. In the spring, before the ice and snow have melted, the plant starts to grow. In its growth heat is produced, and this heat is sufficient to melt the ice which covers the plant. As growth proceeds and the stem grows upward, the heat generated by the growing plant melts a path straight upward through the ice until the plant reaches the air. During all this time the thick leaves which grew close to the ground the previous summer are giving up their stores of food. As a consequence they shrink in size until they are mere skeletons of what they were at first.

Do we too store starch and oil? Yes. Lying immediately under the-skin of all well fed people, and well fed animals, you find a layer of fat, and fat also is stored around the kidneys. Another substance, animal starch, is stored in the liver and in the muscles

Now this storing of fat and starch in the human body is a very vital matter. The animal starch, or "glycogen," as it is generally called, is stored for but a short time. More or less of it is turned into sugar and carried by the blood to the muscles, nerves, and other parts of the body, where it burns and gives rise to the heat of the body and to muscular movements.

But in the case of fat, the storing is much more permanent. People do not suddenly grow very thin or grow very fat. What variations there are go on so slowly that well fed, healthy adults do not change much in weight for months at a time, or even years. But let a prolonged illness come on, and it will soon be seen that the fat underneath the skin gradually becomes used up in feeding the rest of the body : slowly but surely people become reduced almost to skin and bone.

When a person takes consumption it is a matter of great importance whether he has much or little fat stored away in his body ; because, as the disease makes progress, the patient always loses weight; in fact loss of weight and a persistent cough are at first usually, but not always, the only symptoms of this disease.    If, therefore, the patient is stout, that is, has some surplus fat to draw upon while fighting the disease, he has just so much the better chance of recovery.

In treating this disease one of the first things that a physician does is to feed his patient with the most nourishing and easily digested diet which can be procured, in order to improve his general health and increase his power of resisting the disease.    In fighting consumption one of the first signs of improvement is increase of the patient's weight.

When man uses for food the materials which plants and animals have stored for themselves or for their offspring, he is doing what is quite right ; because, of course, he cannot live upon sunlight, air, and soil, as plants do.    He must have other materials for food.    But when he uses these stored materials for the purpose of manufacturing different kinds of drinks containing alcohol, there does not appear to be any doubt that he is misusing Nature's gifts.

Man uses barley, rye, oats, Indian corn and other cereals for making different kinds of ale, beer, and whisky.    The brewer keeps barley in a warm moist room for some days, during which it sprouts, just as if it were in warm moist soil.    As the sprouting goes on much of the starch is turned into sugar.    The grain is then dried in a kiln to stop its further growth, and after being ground into a kind of meal, it is placed in large vats and water added to it so as to dissolve the sugar.

To this solution of sugar the brewer adds yeast, which is a tiny plant smaller than mould ; and, as soon as he has done this, a sort of boiling process begins, known as fermentation, alcohol being formed and also much carbon dioxide.  The fermentation is similar to what takes place in grape juice when wine is made, and also to what takes place when "home made" wine is made from raspberry or currant juice.  In all these cases fermentation occurs and goes on until the alcohol amounts to about 13 per cent. of the whole solution.

The fermented liquid thus formed from barley is used in making beer, ale, or whisky, as the manufacturer may decide.  If beer is desired, hops are added and some other processes carried out which are known to those engaged in this trade.

If, however, whisky is to be made, the liquid is subjected to a very different process, known as distillation. This is done by means of a still. The fermented liquid from the barley is put into the still and the whisky is distilled off. The similar process of distilling

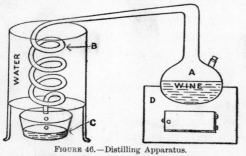

FIGURE 46.—Distilling Apparatus.

brandy from fermented grape juice is shown in the accompanying illustration.  The juice is placed in the part A, and heated over a fire in D. The alcohol comes away in the form of a fine mist, or vapour, and in the coil B, which is surrounded with cold water to condense the vapour, it is turned into the liquid, whisky, and drops into the vessel C.

It is stated that no less than 65,000,000 bushels of barley is produced annually in Great Britain to make liquors of various kinds, and 32,000,000 imported from other countries for the same purpose. In addition to these, it is well known that inferior grades of whisky are manufactured from cheap substitutes, such as Indian corn and refuse molasses.

Many of the cheap whiskies are much more harmful to health than pure malt whisky, which is the kind made from barley. Accordingly, if whisky is prescribed by a physician for any reason, care should be taken to see that only the purest malt whisky is used.

As it takes six pounds of barley to make one gallon of ale, and a gallon of ale contains only about half a pound of solid matter, consisting of salts, curdy matter and sugar, it can readily be seen how terribly wasteful it is to turn barley into ale. A gallon of ale does not contain the tithe of the nourishment that six pounds of barley do, and is no equivalent at all as food for human beings or domestic animals.

It is important to note the great difference between fermented liquors like ales and wines on the one hand, and distilled liquors like whisky, brandy and rum on the other. The former contain much smaller quantities of alcohol; in fact, we may roughly classify alcoholic liquors

into three groups according to the quantity of alcohol
they contain :

1. Beers, porters, stout, etc., containing from 4 to 7
per cent. of alcohol.

2. Wines, such as port wine, sherry, claret, champagne
and " home made " wines, containing variously from 5 to
22 per cent. of alcohol.

3. Spirits, or distilled liquors, containing from 40 to 56
per cent. of alcohol.

The importance of the distinction between fermented
and distilled liquors becomes clear when we learn that,
as a general rule, people begin by drinking the weaker
liquors, ales, beer, and wine. At first the weaker
liquors satisfy the taste for alcohol. But, as time goes
on, the taste for alcohol grows stronger. Then the
drinker of ale and wine may become the drinker of
whisky and brandy, and before he knows it, he is in
the grip of the alcohol habit.

This unfortunate and degrading habit has sometimes
been started among boys and young men in boarding-
schools or colleges. In some of these, beer is upon the
dinner-table as a regular beverage. No wonder then
that, in the course of a few years, some of the graduates
pass into the drunkard's grave.

## CHAPTER XXIV

### ALCOHOL AND BODY HEAT

How do we regulate the heat in a school-room?

If the room becomes too warm, the windows are opened so as to allow the heated air to escape. In addition to this, the damper of the stove or furnace is closed so as to shut off the draught ; thus, less air reaches the wood or coal, and less heat is produced ; so that between the opening of the windows and the decrease in the burning, the room soon cools down and becomes more comfortable.

On the other hand, what is done when the room is too cold? In this case the windows, if open, are closed. This prevents the escape of some of the heat; but, besides this, the damper of the stove or furnace is opened, so that more air reaches the wood or coal and causes the fire to burn up more brightly. Thus, more heat is produced and the room grows warmer.

The temperature of the body tends to rise and fall in much the same way as does that of a room. When a person suffers from fever, his temperature often rises as high as 104° or 105° F. ; when he has been exposed to prolonged cold, as he is when he passes the night in a drunken sleep without shelter, his temperature may fall to 95° F. or even lower. These, however, are unusual variations. In a state of health, so nicely are the gain and the loss of body-heat regulated that the temperature remains almost exactly the same—98.4° F., all the year round. Now, this cannot be the case unless there is some mechanism by which our bodies make more heat or less heat, as stoves do ; and some other mechanism by which they keep in the heat or lose the heat, as rooms do. It would be a very bad thing for us if our bodies did not possess some power of regulating their heat.

And so they do. Our bodies are burning all the time and giving out heat, but not always at the same rate. At some times they make much more heat than at others. In fact, when we are in good health, they keep changing the amount of heat according to the weather. On a cold day or in a cold room, our bodies make more heat. On a warm day or in a warm room, they make less heat.

How is this done? By our bodies acting in much the same way as a stove is made to act. When our bodies tend to become cold, messages go along nerves from the skin to the spinal cord without our being conscious of them. As a result of this, other messages go from the spinal cord out to the muscles of the chest, and we breathe faster or deeper; that is, we take in more air, just as a stove does when the damper is opened. The burning therefore goes on more quickly in our bodies, and more heat is produced.

While the breathing becomes quickened, the blood-vessels also lying in and under the skin grow smaller; so that less blood goes to the surface, and therefore less heat is lost. In fact, our bodies regulate the heat in nearly the same way as a wise teacher regulates the heat in a school. Only there is this difference; the making of more or less heat in the body, and the loss of more or less heat from the skin, are both regulated by the nerves of the body without our being conscious of the changes.

The watery part of sweat plays a very important part in regulating the heat of the body; because, as the sweat comes out on the skin it evaporates; that is, it dries up and passes into the air. Now in order to change from liquid sweat to vapour of water, heat is required and this heat is withdrawn from the body. Consequently, our bodies are greatly cooled by the evaporation of perspiration.

As there is very little evaporation of sweat from the skin of dogs, the loss of heat from their bodies takes place chiefly by evaporation of moisture from the mouth, throat, windpipe, and bronchial tubes. The faster dogs breathe the more quickly evaporation goes on, and the more they are cooled. This accounts for their rapid breathing in hot weather; they are cooling themselves.

Now, if you understand how the body regulates its own heat, you will have no trouble in understanding how alcohol affects the heat of the body in winter.

As everyone knows, some people drink whisky or brandy in cold weather, because they think it makes them warm. Now, what the whisky really does is this: acting through the nerves, it widens the bore of the blood-vessels of the skin and allows more blood to pass to the surface, as may be seen at any time in the flushed face of one who habitually uses it. If the weather is cold, this blood becomes much cooled, because it is so near the surface; and when it returns to the windpipe, lungs, and intestines, it cools them below their natural temperature. The consequence is that these organs may develop such diseases as bronchitis, pneumonia, or diarrhœa. Thus, the whisky actually upsets the healthy working of the heat apparatus of our bodies. In place of helping to keep the body warm, it really makes it cold.

Those who travel in arctic regions now-a-days never drink alcohol in order to keep warm. Dr. Carpenter tells about a crew of sixty-six men who left Denmark and wintered in Hudson Bay. They took an abundant supply of alcohol with them, thinking that it would help them to keep warm. By the end of the winter they were all dead but two men, because the alcohol had destroyed the power of their bodies to regulate their temperature.

As an example of how the very opposite practice turned out, an English crew of twenty-two men wintered just as far north as the Danish crew, but they used no alcohol. In the spring, twenty of them were alive and well. The heat apparatus of their bodies had been left uninjured by alcohol, and this had helped them to pass the cold winter there without any harm.

We may keep the heat apparatus of our bodies in good working order by taking good care of our general health, and by taking a cool bath every morning if we are strong enough to stand one. The bath stimulates the nerves which control the heat apparatus, so that this apparatus is always ready to generate more heat or less heat when required. Besides this the bath alters the blood supply to the skin, so that it gives off heat or retains heat just as may be needed.

Nor does alcohol make us cool in hot weather, as some drinkers would have us believe ; in fact, it slows down the circulation of the blood, because it decreases the force of the heart-beat. The heat will thus tend to accumulate in the body, and in very hot weather this would help to produce heatstroke. The effects of alcohol, therefore, are bad whether we drink it in winter or in summer.

## CHAPTER XXV

### EXERCISE AND SLEEP

The bones of the body when joined together in their natural positions form what is known as the skeleton.

Suppose you were thinking of the skeleton as lying down, and were devising some plan to enable it to remain standing upright if it were once placed upon its feet.   How would it do to arrange straps in pairs all the way up the length of the back and front of the body? The front straps would prevent the skeleton from falling backward, and the back straps would prevent it from falling forward.   Additional straps would have to be attached up the side of each leg and also up each side of the trunk to prevent it from falling sideways.   Actually in a way similar to this, the muscles are attached to the bones and act upon them so as to make the skeleton retain an upright position.   Besides, they overlie the skeleton and along with the fat give roundness to the form.   But muscles do something more than this : they make the body move.   In producing bodily movement, muscles usually act in pairs or in sets.   For example, when the set of muscles along the front of the forearm contracts or shortens, the fingers are drawn down so as to touch the palm of the hand.   When an opposite set on the back of the forearm contracts, the set on the front relaxes or lengthens, and the fingers again become straight.   Similarly, the bending of the forearm toward the upper arm is caused by the biceps muscle, a mass of lean meat which you can feel at the front of the arm between the shoulder and the elbow.   When this mass shortens and thickens it pulls upon a bone immediately

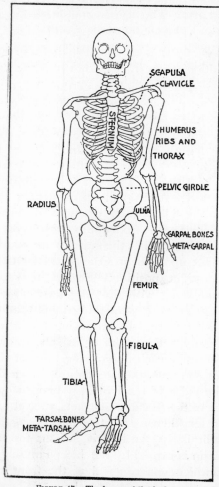

FIGURE 47.—The bones of the body.

below the elbow, and the forearm is thus drawn upward to the upper arm. The arm is straightened again by the contraction of a muscle on the opposite side of the upper arm. Whenever, therefore, movement of the body takes place, one muscle or set of muscles shortens and an opposite muscle or set of muscles lengthens. If this were not the case, no movement of the body would be possible.

A muscle which contracts when we *will* that it should contract, is known as a "voluntary muscle." Most of the muscles of the arms, legs, and trunk are of this kind. In the innermost parts of the body, however, as in the intestines, there are other muscles which contract without our being conscious of their movements. These are known as "involuntary muscles."

When the muscles of the trunk are not properly trained there is a faulty carriage or a slouchy walk. Either (1) the head hangs forward, or (2) the shoulders are round or "stooped," or (3) one shoulder is higher than the other, or (4) the whole backbone or spine is curved to one side, or (5) the backbone has too slight a curvature at the loins. Of course there are other forms of curvature of the spine which are not due to muscular weakness and which can not be cured by muscular training.

Certain occupations, as, for example, sewing, gardening, and lifting heavy weights

FIGURE 48.—Right position at a school-desk.

are liable to make people round-shouldered; but this tendency may be corrected by exercising the muscles of the back so as to keep the body straight. Unsuitable school furniture also, especially when children are writing or drawing, tends to produce bodily deformities of different kinds.

Young people who have any of these defects should ask their teacher how they may be remedied; and, if the teacher cannot suggest the proper muscular training, the pupil should go to a doctor for advice.

Round shoulders cause compression of the top of the lungs, with a tendency to lung disease. Again, an inerect carriage allows the intestines to settle down into the pelvis with a likelihood sooner or later of disease of the internal organs. Both defects can easily be remedied by careful attention to muscular exercise.

In contrast with an inerect carriage, not merely is the erect one healthful; it also helps us to maintain our self-respect and to command the respect of others. On the other hand, a lounging gait often excites ridicule or mild contempt.

The use or disuse of an organ produces a very great influence on the organ itself. When properly used the organ grows in size and vigour, whereas, when improperly used, or not used at all, it tends to lose the power it should naturally possess.

FIGURE 49.—Wrong position at a school-desk.

The descendants of fish which have lived for ages in a dark cave have in the course of many generations become blind, because their eyes have had no exercise.  In the same way muscles that have had no exercise for a considerable length of time slowly lose their size and strength.   In fact, all power of moving a limb is sometimes lost, as is the case when a joint has been kept unused for a long time. Indeed exercise of our muscles is more necessary for the general health than exercise of the eye or of the ear, useful as these latter may be.

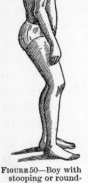

FIGURE 50—Boy with stooping or round-shoulders.

To realize this it is only necessary to learn that there is always present in the skeletal muscles about one-quarter of the blood of the body.  This large blood supply shows what important organs the muscles are.  Now, when muscles contract, either voluntarily or involuntarily the blood-vessels are pressed by the intervening muscles and the blood is forced onward in its circulation.   In other words, muscular contraction is an important aid to the circulation of the blood.   On the other hand, sitting still, that is, taking no exercise will tend to allow the blood to stagnate, and as you will remember from the chapter on the circulation,

FIGURE 51.—Boy with erect carriage.

stagnation of blood will lead to impaired excretion of waste, to lack of proper nutrition, and to lack of vigorous growth.

And this brings up the question of how much exercise young people should take, and what kind of exercise. In answer it must be said that the kind of exercise and its amount depend upon a number of things. For example, they depend upon whether one is well-formed and strong, or ill-shaped and delicate.

For those who are round-shouldered, a special set of exercises should be planned by a teacher or a doctor and carried on for a long time. Those who have an awkward gait should practise special exercises, so that, in time, heavy lumbering movements may be thrown off, or perhaps changed to graceful ones. But such special exercises are for the few only.

Most young people will get the greatest benefit from a combination of exercises such as are furnished by gymnastics or calisthenics on the one hand, and by games on the other. Each kind has its own special advantage. A properly graded course in gymnastics or calisthenics develops all the muscles of the body symmetrically; whereas games do not. As you will no doubt remember, the skeletal muscles nearly all act in sets or in pairs, hence, all those exercises which call into play the muscles of the arms, legs, and trunk, at regular intervals and in regular order, must tend to an all-round development of every muscle of the body.

Games on the contrary usually call into play special sets of muscles, and, of course, develop these more than the rest For example, in playing baseball it is the muscles of the right hand, right arm, and right half of the trunk that are chiefly used. The same thing is true of hockey and lacrosse. Hence, these games and others like them tend to develop a slightly lop-sided, or unsymmetrical body. But notwithstanding this obvious drawback, it is nevertheless true that games furnish the best exercise of all for both boys and girls.

A word or two may here be said about military drill. Military drill certainly gives exercise to the muscles; but as for muscular exercise for boys and girls, neither military drill nor gymnastics are so good as lawn tennis, baseball, lacrosse, football, basket ball, or other games in which they are interested. It is true that military drill makes pupils walk erect, inculcates prompt obedience, and develops uniformly most of the muscles of the body; but drill should not be practised by pupils to the exclusion of exercises which they plan for themselves.

One very great advantage of games over routine drill, whether military or gymnastic, is that they exercise both mind and muscles; whereas drill and class gymnastics, once they have been learned, exercise the muscles only.

To sum up, exercise of the muscles may be used for two or three very different purposes:

In the first place, it may be used to strengthen certain muscles of the body; as, for example, the muscles of the back, so as to prevent a person from being round-shouldered.

In the second place, exercises may be used to remedy a faulty carriage or an awkward gait. But only a few boys and girls need exercises to correct either of these defects, because only a few have them.

In the third place, we may exercise both muscles and mind in sports for the sake of taking care of our health,—a purpose quite different from the other two. Along with such sports we may include the healthful practice of exercising the muscles for ten or fifteen minutes every morning before dressing, and also all exercises that will give us pleasure and at the same time call into play the faculties of the mind.

And if, in taking exercise in any way, we strive with others and try to excel, no harm will be done so long as we do not carry the struggle too far. The important matter is to get the exercise, while all the time we keep the mastery over ourselves, and do not overstrain our nerves and muscles, thus bringing on disease of the heart, blood-vessels, or other organs.

But in order to keep in good health not merely must we have exercise of the muscles, we must have rest of the muscles and rest of the brain as well. Now the best rest for both is sleep.

How much sleep should we have? The number of hours will vary with the individual. Young people need more than adults. Children of ten and eleven years of age should have about eleven or twelve hours; older school children, from nine to ten; and grown-up people, from seven to eight hours. The aged and delicate require more sleep than the strong.

Young people are not usually troubled with sleeplessness; but it is well that they should know how to avoid it. In the first place, they should take plenty of exercise in the fresh air, which is almost the same as saying that they should not work long hours at any indoor occupation. Nor should they worry over their work after leaving the school, office, or factory.

There should be a fixed hour for going to bed every night and for getting up in the morning. The bed should be clean and somewhat hard, and it should have a low pillow. It is better to lie upon either the right or the left side, than upon the back. The foot of the bed should be nearest the stove or other source of heat, and the window should be open all night—more widely in summer than in winter. Neither cold air nor night air can do harm, if one is covered with plenty of bed-clothes. In very cold weather a light cap should be worn to avoid the danger of catching a cold in the head. If you follow all these rules and are still troubled with sleeplessness, it is time for you to consult a physician.

Again, some people who have been much troubled with sleeplessness have taken drugs known as "sleeping powders" in order to get sleep. But the danger of forming the habit of using sleeping powders is very great, and, when once the habit has been formed, it is very hard to fall asleep without their use. As time goes on, the users of these drugs find that they have to take more and more of them, until finally their health is destroyed. No sleeping powders should ever be used except by the order of a physician.

## CHAPTER XXVI

### ✕ CLOTHING

When warming yourself in the sun, did it ever occur to you to ask how the heat travels from the sun to the earth? Or have you ever considered how heat passes from the stove at one end of the school-room to the other end?

With a little help from your teacher you will learn that heat is lost from the school stove in at least two ways. In the first place the heat warms the air above and around the stove, and this warm air rises to the ceiling and spreads throughout the room. This way of spreading heat is known as "convection." In the next place some more heat is lost by the stove sending it out in straight lines, "radiating" it we say, in all directions, just as the sun does when his warm rays reach the earth.

Now, our bodies also lose heat by convection and radiation, and in two other ways besides; namely, by the drying up or evaporation of the sweat which comes out on the skin, and by the heat passing through our clothing from the skin to the outside. This latter and fourth way of losing heat is spoken of as "conduction."

You may understand what is meant by conduction of heat if you simply place one end of a long iron poker in a fire, and note how the heat slowly travels from the end that is in the fire away out toward the other. In the same way some of the heat of the body warms the clothing that is next the skin, and then slowly travels outwards through the clothing toward the air.

Of course, the speed at which the heat travels from the skin outwards will not be always the same. It will vary with the kind of clothing we wear, just as the speed at which heat travels along a wire varies with the kind of metal ; for heat is conducted along a copper wire faster than along an iron one. And in much the same way the heat of the body will travel to the outside air through cotton or linen clothing faster than through wool or fur.

It has, accordingly, been found that linen and cotton are the most suitable for summer clothing, because they are cool, that is, because they quickly conduct the heat away from the body ; while wool and fur are the most suitable for winter, because they are warm, that is, because they keep in the heat of the body.

We must remember these facts about the conduction of heat, because the suitability of any clothing material depends largely upon its power of preventing the heat of the body from escaping. As the temperature of the human body is 98.4° F., while that of the air in this country is rarely higher than 90° F., it follows that the inside of our clothing is usually warmer than the outside. We must, therefore, always wear clothing which is suited to the season. In summer it must consist of material that is a good conductor of heat, that is, material which will keep in only a very little of the body heat ; whereas, in winter it must consist of material which is a poor conductor, that is, which will keep in most of the body heat.

Whether for winter or for summer use, clothing should always be as light as possible. Some people have an idea that clothing should be light for summer use and heavy for winter. But the fact is that clothing of heavy but good conducting material may not be so warm for winter use as light clothing made of non-conducting material.

Warm clothing is made of non-conducting material;—it is full of fine pores or meshes. As these are being filled with imprisoned air which is a bad conductor of heat, it follows that light porous material will be the best for keeping in the heat of our bodies. Of course, when it is very cold, fur is the best clothing, because the wind cannot pass through the skin part. But excepting in extremely cold weather, and in rainy weather when we wear waterproof material, clothing should be porous in order to allow the sweat to evaporate freely.

Clothing should also be loose. Tight gloves and tight shoes keep the warm blood away from the hands and feet and as a consequence we suffer from the cold. In the same way tight clothing tends to make the body cold in cold weather.

But tight clothing is objectionable for another reason. Tight hats and caps impede the circulation of the blood to the scalp and cause baldness; and tight collars impede the circulation to the head and cause headache. Tight belts, waistcoats, or waists lessen the size of the lower part of the chest and of the upper part of the abdomen, thus seriously interfering with the healthy working of the lungs, heart, stomach, and intestines, and causing sometimes life-long suffering. In young people the narrow waist is generally the forerunner of indigestion, weakness, nervous debility, and consumption. So important is this matter of loose clothing thought to be in England, that, in some of the largest and best boarding-schools, the boys are not allowed to wear waistcoats and belts at all.

Not merely should clothing be loose, but, as I have said, it should be as light as possible, and such weight as

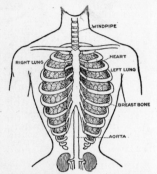

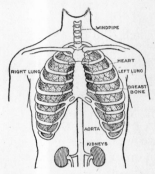

FIGURE 52.—The effect of tight cloth-ing on the chest.

FIGURE 53.—Natural shape of chest.

it possesses should be borne mainly by the shoulders. Heavy clothing that is carried by bands round the waist, tends to displace the internal organs and bring on disease.

The aged, the delicate, and the very young should wear thin under-flannel the year round—dry, loose, and warm. One reason for wearing it in summer is that it generally prevents the bad effects of sudden changes of tempera-ture. A slight drawback to its use is that it absorbs the sweat slowly.

We should never keep on under-garments that have become damp with either rain or sweat, because the evaporation of the moisture, whether rain or sweat, chills the body. Wet garments should be changed for dry as soon as possible. If this can not be done, we should not sit down in them, especially if a wind is blowing; but should rather walk about until they are dry.

Once more, clothing should be warm enough to keep us from catching cold. Many young people expose their necks to cold winds in winter, and as a result catch cold in the nose or throat. The redness, swelling, and pain which may result, indicate that these parts are weak and unable to throw off the effects of disease germs In very cold weather, therefore, every person should wear a muffler or other adequate protection for the throat. A succession of colds generally brings on chronic catarrh, a diseased condition of the nose and throat which causes a very offensive breath. A cold of course never gives us consumption or any other disease; but it alters the juices or watery secretions of the nose, throat, and windpipe, so that they no longer kill disease germs, as they do when we are in good health.

For more than half the year some kind of footwear is an absolute necessity in our climate in order to keep the feet warm. But the selection of boots and shoes rarely receives much attention. Quite frequently children make their own selection, and do it so badly that a great deal of discomfort is the result. Ill-fitting shoes worn by children for several years show the effects of slight steady pressure in changing the shape of the foot. As a rule, the pressure is never great enough to cause much pain. The child does not say that the shoes are hurting his feet. But the pressure applied day after day, for months and years, slowly presses the big toe over toward the outer side of the foot and away from the straight line in which it always lies in the infant. Sometimes the little toe also is pressed toward the inner side of the foot. These two changes, one in the big toe and the other in the little toe, are always the result of wearing boots or shoes with narrow toes. So much have our feet been altered by the pressure of ill-fitting boots or shoes, that it is a rare thing to find a man's or a woman's foot well-shaped.

What should be the shape of a shoe which would not alter the shape of the foot? No doubt, different

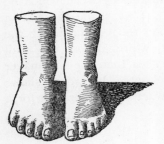

shoemakers would answer this question in different ways. But surely a common sense way of fixing upon the right shape would be to say that the

FIGURE 54.—Infant's feet.

FIG. 55.—Adult foot.

outline of the natural foot should determine the outline of the well-fitting shoe.

If we covered the whole of the sole of the foot with printer's ink, or some kind of soft paint, or even water, and then planted the foot upon a sheet of white paper, placed on the floor, we should get a shape, not of the outline of the whole foot, but of those parts of the foot which press upon the paper. If then we drew a line around the outside of the figure thus printed upon the paper, we should get the correct shape for the sole of a shoe.

If we fix upon the shape in this way, then it will differ somewhat from that given by most shoe-

FIG. 56.    FIG. 57.
Two different shapes for the sole of a boot. Which should you select? Why?

makers. The outline will be curved inwards much more on the inner side, and curved outwards much more on the outer side of the foot. A shoe shaped upon this outline will take into account those parts of the sole of the foot upon which the weight of the body falls, as well as the arch of the foot on its inner side upon which no weight falls. If we shape the sole of our shoes upon the outline which the foot prints upon a sheet of white paper, we shall certainly get a better shaped shoe than the shoemaker gives us in his sharp-pointed boots. Figure 56 shows the proper shape of a boot, whether for a man or for a woman.

It is only right, however, to say that within the past few years considerable improvement has been made in the shape of children's footwear. The so-called leather sandals are much to be commended for summer wear. Their shape is like that of the foot, while their coolness and facility for ventilation and evaporation through the openings in the leather leave little to be desired.

FIGURE 58.—High heel boot.

Improvement in women's footwear has not kept pace with that in children's. In the case of the former the most objectionable features are the high heel and pointed toe. The effect of the high heel is to thrust the foot toward the toe of the boot, thus displacing both the big toe and the little one and producing corns and bunions. A further objection is that the weight of the body is thrown largely upon the toes.

---

## CHAPTER XXVII

 PURE AND IMPURE WATER

Where shall we find pure water? Rarely in surface wells; because in the past they have not always been dug far enough away from the barn-yard, the kitchen, or the privy vault. As a result, filthy surface water leaks in at the top, or passes through the adjacent soil into the water which lies under the ground.

Nor can it always be obtained from springs; because cattle are frequently allowed to stand around these and pollute them with their filth, or surface drainage from higher ground may mingle with the spring and poison it at its source.

So careless are many farmers about the location and surroundings of their wells, that typhoid fever has come to be pre-eminently a disease of country districts. Every autumn there are thousands of cases of it among the farmers of this continent.

A polluted water with few germs in it may not of itself produce an outbreak of typhoid directly, but it may do so through the medium of the milk supply. How this may happen can be very easily explained. If the milk is pure, that is, if it comes from healthy cows, it cannot give typhoid fever to any one. But, if milk cans are washed out, as they sometimes are, with water which contains typhoid germs and which has not been sterilized by boiling, then the germs in even the few drops of water which remain in the can may increase vastly in number in the milk which is afterwards put into the can. The fact is that typhoid germs grow better in warm milk than in anything else. Enormous numbers of them may

FIGURE 59.—The well, pig-pen, and waste water are too near together. The light shading below the surface shows how the filth from both sides joins the ground water and thus enters the well. *A B* vertical section through the ground. *B C* ground water.

develop in the milk from a few drops of infected water; and, if this polluted milk is drunk, it becomes the means of setting up the disease just as surely as infected water does.

How many of the germs of typhoid fever must a person take in drinking water, in food, or in milk, before

the disease is set up in his body? The number will
vary much in different people, because some people
are born strong, and others delicate ; some people take
good care of their health, and others are quite careless
about it; some again follow a healthful calling, and others
follow an unhealthful one. Moreover, some people are
poorly housed, ill-clothed, and ill-fed. Hence, it always
comes to pass that, in an outbreak of any infectious
disease, the sickly, delicate, or ill-cared for are the ones
who suffer most.

When we learn that cold cannot kill the germs
of typhoid fever, and that they may therefore lie
dormant on the snow, or be frozen in ice all winter ;
when, in addition, we learn that a person who has
had typhoid fever continues to pass the germs from
his intestines even for years after he has recovered
from the disease, we can readily see how difficult a
matter it must be to prevent the germs from leaking
into wells during heavy rains or spring freshets, or
draining into rivers and lakes, and thus keeping the
disease alive from season to season.

In cities and towns, it is not wise for the householders
to have their own wells ; because it has been found that
when houses are crowded together along the streets,
the well-water becomes very impure on account of
the filth that gets into it from the surface.

For this reason, in all cities and in most towns, each
house gets its drinking water from underground pipes
which bring pure water from lakes or streams at some
distance from the town.

But the houses in all cities and most towns have a
second set of pipes, called " sewer-pipes." These gather

up the polluted water from every house and carry it away into larger pipes under the streets.

Of course this polluted water or "sewage" should always be disposed of in such a way that it will do no harm to any citizen. But this is not always done. When poured into a river, it is likely to pollute the water for citizens of other towns lower down the stream; and

FIGURE 60.—Water-tank, water-pipes, and sewer-pipes for a town. The water-pipes are shown as lying at a higher level than the sewer-pipes. Of course, both are underground in all towns and cities.

when poured into the lake or bay upon which the town itself is situated, it may pollute the water supply for its own citizens if they get their water supply from the lake or bay.

Years ago, it was a common belief that running water, even if polluted up stream, always became pure in the course of its journey down stream. This belief, however, was pretty thoroughly dispelled about twenty

years ago because of a number of outbreaks of typhoid
fever which occurred in different cities along the banks
of the Merrimac river.

Take the following map of the State of Massachusetts
and note the course of this river. Note also some
of the towns and cities that are situated upon its banks.
At the mouth is Newburyport with a population of

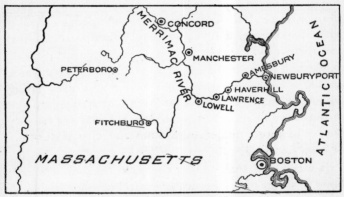

FIGURE 61.—Map of Merrimac River.

14,000; Amesbury further up with 11,000; next,
Haverhill, 30,000; then Lawrence, 46,900; and lastly,
Lowell, 84,000.

In the autumn of 1890, Lowell suffered from a severe
outbreak of typhoid fever. There were, in all, 550 cases
with 92 deaths :—

|  | CASES. |
| --- | --- |
| In September | 47 |
| October | 95 |
| November | 171 |
| December | 159 |
| January | 78 |
| Total | 550 |

The usual long list of causes was given for the outbreak; it was said to be due to impure well water, to impure city water, to bad drainage, to sewers or sewer gas, to infected milk, to infected vegetables, and to impure ice. Which of these was the true cause, it was left to Professor W. T. Sedgwick, of the Massachusetts State Board of Health to find out. His first step was to engage assistants to visit every house in the city. They were instructed to find out how many people were ill with the disease, and where they obtained their water and their milk.

Most of the patients drank water from the city waterworks, a few used wells, and fewer still used spring water that had been brought from a distance and sold in bottles. The cases were widely spread over the city, but were more numerous around the city water-tank, or reservoir.

It was found that among the sick, the only common bond was the drinking water, and Professor Sedgwick started to look for the cause of the disease in the city water. The mouth of the intake pipe, through which water was pumped up to the reservoir, lay in the Merrimac river, about half a mile above the city.

If you were yourselves hunting for the source of the disease you would naturally think that the germs must have entered the river somewhere above the end of the intake pipe; and sure enough, it was up the river that the source of the pollution was found.

Three miles above Lowell, a small dirty stream, called Stony Brook, joins the Merrimac river. At this point, is the village of North Chelmsford, whose workingmen are chiefly mill-hands. The drainage of the village is passed into Stony Brook, and flows thence into the Merrimac, and down the river toward Lowell. Had there been any typhoid in North Chelmsford before the outbreak at Lowell?

Careful inquiries in the village brought out the fact that on July 27th there had been a *suspected* case. On August 24th, there was an undoubted case. The patient, though ailing, had kept at work in a mill until August 23rd. On September 6th, there was another case. Two brothers, one of whom died, were ill with the disease between September 23rd and October 30th. Both of these, although ill, continued at work, and both used water-closets which overhung Stony Brook, for probably two weeks before they took to bed. In short, there was an outbreak of typhoid fever in North Chelmsford before the outbreak in Lowell, and there is no doubt that the cause of the one was the cause of the other.

Did the Lowell cases give rise to additional cases among the inhabitants of Lawrence, and of other towns further down the river? Here again, the facts speak for themselves. Lowell, in 1890, passed its sewage into the Merrimac, just as did the other towns along its banks. This sewage must have contained the germs of typhoid, and being passed into the river without being disinfected, some of the germs would be likely to get into the drinking water of people living in the city of Lawrence.

Lawrence lies nine miles below Lowell. Would the water become purified in running this distance? It would seem not, because the outbreak in Lowell was followed by one in Lawrence. It was of a mild type, and was at its worst during November and December.

All who had the disease drank the city water, and there were, as in Lowell, more cases in houses immediately around the reservoir. Lastly, after the disease ceased in Lowell, it gradually ceased in Lawrence.

The record of cases reported by the physicians in Lowell, Lawrence, and Newburyport in 1892 and 1893 shows this very clearly.

|  | LOWELL | LAWRENCE | NEWBURYPORT |
|---|---|---|---|
| November, 1892.... | 19 | 14 | 0 |
| December, " .... | 70 | 32 | 4 |
| January, 1893...... | 38 | 72 | 28 |
| February, " ...... | 14 | 23 | 9 |

These facts point to but one conclusion, namely, that running water does not always purify itself.

One would naturally like to know why there were not many more cases in Lawrence than in Lowell, when so many more persons were sick in Lowell than in North Chelmsford, and, therefore, so many more germs must have been passed with the Lowell sewage water into the river below.

But, in the first place, we must remember that North Chelmsford is only three miles above Lowell, whereas Lawrence is nine miles below it. The number of germs, therefore, in the water below Lowell, would be widely spread throughout a large volume, and the chance of taking in enough germs at Lawrence to produce fever would, as a result, be much lessened. Moreover, some of them are probably killed by the oxygen dissolved in the water, and others die from lack of food.

## CHAPTER XXVIII

### LAKE WATER

The water from a large lake is no safer to drink than river water unless care is taken to prevent the pollution of the part that supplies the drinking water. This was strikingly shown in yearly outbreaks of typhoid fever that took place in Kingston, Ontario, from 1889 to 1892. At that time the city derived its water-supply from Lake Ontario. The intake pipe through which water was pumped all over the city ran out into the bay a distance of only 150 yards from the shore. Not far from the end of the suction pipe a large drain discharged sewage from the general hospital and from a number of private dwellings. Farther west, sewage from a large jail and from the hospital for the insane was emptied into the bay. It must be borne in mind also that the current which sets eastward past Kingston into the St. Lawrence river is a very slow one. The water in the harbour might be looked upon as almost standing still. Taking all these facts together, it will readily be seen that the water which was supplied to Kingston for some years could not have been good.

The citizens became greatly alarmed when they learned that the discharges from typhoid fever patients were emptied into closets and passed thence through drains into the sluggish waters of the bay near the intake pipe. These discharges should have been made harmless by mixing them with chemicals, like chloride of lime or carbolic acid, so as to kill the germs ; but this was not done. Only one result could follow ; the germs were drawn up again from the bay in the suction pipe, and spread all over the city in its drinking water.

The citizens were warned not to drink the city water unless it were well boiled. But boiling the Kingston water was only a makeshift. The health of the citizens demanded that they should have pure water. They,

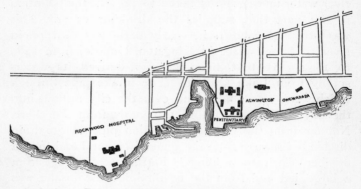

FIGURE 62.—Western end of Kingston Harbour.

therefore, had the intake pipe laid away out in the bay over a mile from the shore, so as to extend quite beyond where the lake water was likely to be polluted with city sewage. As a result the annual outbreaks of typhoid fever ceased.

Very few cases of this fever occurred in Kingston again until the early part of the winter of 1902. Suddenly a number of cases occurred in different parts of the city. The citizens were again warned to boil their water, and meanwhile the city doctors and the local board of health set to work to find out the source of the infection.

After a good deal of work, the cause was discovered. There was a leak in the suction pipe not far from the shore. During one of the autumn gales, a vessel had

come into the harbour for shelter and had cast anchor
not far away from the intake pipe. The anchor did not
hold fast, and the vessel dragged it along the bottom

FIGURE 63.—Eastern end of Kingston Harbour.

until the anchor caught on the suction pipe. The pipe
was pulled away to one side, so that the bolts at one of
the joints gave way. The result was that an opening
about three inches wide was made at the joint, and
through this some of the filthy water coming from the
city drains was drawn up into the water-pipes. As soon
as the damage was repaired, the outbreak also ceased.

Toronto, Cleveland, and Chicago have all had a similar
experience to that of Kingston. In each of the three
places, the city sewage was discharged directly into
the lake or bay. This polluted the water of the bay,
and when this polluted water was again drawn up in
the water-pipes and distributed throughout the city
as drinking water, there could hardly be any other
result than a series of cases of typhoid and a high
yearly death-rate.

Cleveland has solved its water-supply problem by
putting its intake pipe five miles out into the lake, while

Chicago has dug a drainage canal by which it discharges its sewage into the Mississippi river. It still gets its water-supply from Lake Michigan, but it is not now polluted with the city sewage. The water-supply for some large cities is purified by bacteria while it is slowly passing through immense beds of sand and gravel, so that the water flowing away from these "filtration beds" is comparatively free from disease-producing bacteria. Toronto is now building such beds, and when completed they will furnish a relatively pure water-supply for the city. And all the water that is used for drinking purposes in Philadelphia, Lawrence, Albany, Paris, and Hamburg is first purified by passing it through filtration beds. But the safest source of supply for very large cities is a mountain stream or lake, as far away as possible from human dwellings or any other probable source of pollution. Boston, New York, and Liverpool get their water from such sources.

And there are still other sources of water-supply. For example, the Boers in South Africa and the inhabitants of some of the Bermuda Islands, are forced to rely almost entirely upon the rainfall gathered from the roofs of buildings and stored in large tanks. Rain-water is the purest of natural waters, but rain-water caught from roofs may be polluted unless care is taken to keep the roofs clean.

A particularly pure water is that which comes from an artesian well. This differs from the ordinary surface well in the fact that it is sunk much deeper, and usually through rock. Quite often the water rises up several feet above the level of the ground, showing that it has come from some higher locality, usually from a distant mountain. The soakage through the soil for a long distance purifies the water thoroughly from all disease germs. London, Ont., Brooklyn, N. Y., and Lowell, Mass., rely in part upon such wells for their water supply.

Most people have become so impressed with the importance of obtaining pure drinking water, that, whenever they are in doubt about the purity of a particular water they very properly send some of it to a public health officer for examination.

---

## CHAPTER XXIX

### PURE AND IMPURE MILK

You will be surprised to learn that it is quite impossible to milk any cow without allowing some bacteria to get into the milk. The milk pail may be made perfectly clean and free from bacteria, the milker may put on garments of spotless white, his hands may be as clean as soap and water will make them, the stable may be as clean as the cleanest dwelling-house, the cow's body may be washed and groomed until her skin and hair shine like silk ; and yet the milk that streams into the pail may contain hundreds of bacteria in every drop.

Where do they come from ? After a great deal of work by scientific men, it was discovered that bacteria are always present on the udder and within the teats of a cow. These fall into the pail and continue to multiply very rapidly in the warm milk,

The first rule for a milkman to follow, if he wishes to have clean, sweet milk, is to have everything about himself, the stable, and the cow scrupulously clean; the next rule is to throw away the first half-cupful of milk that comes from the udder; and the third rule is to keep the milk cool.

The bacteria that are usually found in cow's milk are known as "lactic acid" bacteria, and their effect upon the milk is to turn it sour, especially in hot weather.

FIGURE 64.—A clean barn-yard.

From all this you will see that there are two great difficulties to be overcome in getting pure milk, namely, the difficulty of keeping it clean and the difficulty of keeping it cool.

It is particularly hard to get pure milk in winter; because cows are generally shut up in dirty stables, or penned in filthy barn-yards. Dust and dirt surround them on all sides and stick to their hair and udders; filth often becomes encrusted upon their sides; the milkers are slovenly and careless; the cows' udders are not washed and dried; and as a result you cannot possibly have clean milk. Milk coming from cows

kept in such surroundings smells musty and has an
animal taste.    It is bad for healthy people ; it is bad for
sick people ; and it is impossible also to make good
butter or cheese from it.

If dirt enters the milk from any source—from the
milker's hands or clothes, from the milk pail or the stable,
from the cow's udder or teats, from musty or dirty food—

FIGURE 65.—A clean cow in tidy surroundings.

then this dirt sows the seeds of bacteria in the milk, and
these bacteria in warm weather grow rapidly and soon
turn the milk sour, slimy, or musty.

Should we not have some standard by which we may
judge of the quality of milk ?   Some people want a law
made that will prevent milkmen from selling milk
unless it contains a certain amount of curdy matter and
a certain amount of fat or cream.   They say nothing

about the amounts of sugar, or salt, or water that this standard milk should contain, but they are strongly of opinion that it should contain not less than 3½ parts of butter fat in every hundred parts of milk.

Now, it is quite right that some standard should be established for milk, but the best standard to fix is one based on cleanliness. Washington, Boston, Rochester,

FIGURE 66.—Clean cows in a clean stable.

and New York have fixed standards of this kind. Rochester does not allow milk to be sold as pure fresh milk, if it contains more than 5,000 bacteria in each drop. New York is not so careful, and has fixed its standard of purity at 50,000 bacteria in each drop.

Washington, D.C., has three standards. Milk of the highest class is known as "certified milk," and must not

contain more than 500 bacteria in each drop; it must
be kept in sterilized bottles at a temperature not over
50° F., and must be delivered to customers within twelve
hours of its being drawn from the cow. The second
standard is known as "inspected milk." This must
contain not more than 5,000 bacteria in each drop; and
must be kept in sterilized vessels at a temperature not

FIGURE 67.—A neat and inexpensive milk house.

exceeding 50° F. Milk of the third standard, containing
as it does more than 5,000 bacteria per drop, must be
pasteurized before it is delivered to the houses of
citizens. You will be told later how milk is pasteurized.

In some cities the milk sold in July and August
is often so filthy that it contains no fewer than
3,500,000 bacteria in each drop. No wonder that the
babies die in hundreds in such cities during these
months.

It is not the heat that is the chief cause of the large number of deaths among infants. No doubt heat does make some of them ill, just as it makes grown-up people ill; but the chief cause of most of the fever and diarrhœa and deaths among infants in summer is impure milk. This has been proved beyond all doubt, because wherever the diet of babies has been changed to clean milk or pasteurized milk the death-rate has at once fallen.

FIGURE 68.—An untidy and unclean milk house.

But bacteria and heat are not the only causes of the high death-rate among babies. Not a few die because of the ignorance or the incapacity of their mothers. Many young mothers have had no training or experience in feeding their infants. They are uncleanly also in their habits and allow the milk to go bad. The consequence is that the little ones are not properly fed.

In order to keep milk from turning sour and to make it keep longer, some milk dealers put chemicals into it. Such milk is known as "adulterated" milk. This practice is forbidden by law in all civilized countries, for the simple reason that such chemical preservatives are usually poisonous.

How is milk pasteurized? Very simply. It is placed in closed sterilized vessels, that is, in vessels that have been washed with boiling water or steam. It is then heated up to 140° F., for twenty minutes, and immediately afterwards cooled down to 50° F.

For pasteurizing large quantities of milk a quicker process than the above has been devised. The milk is passed through a machine which heats it momentarily to a temperature of 167° F., or even higher. It is asserted by milk dealers who practise this process that heating the milk to the higher temperature for a short time has the same effect in killing bacteria as heating the milk to the lower temperature for the

FIGURE 69.—A Clean Milker.

longer time. When this assertion is tested by actual experiment, it is found that the rapid process kills the lactic acid germs only, and not the disease-producing ones. The chief reason why milk dealers practise the rapid process rather than the slower one is because it saves time, and because the milk does not turn sour,—sour milk being a source of great loss to the dealers.

Pasteurized milk is not by any means the best kind of milk; but its use has prevented much sickness among delicate people, and, as has been stated already, it has saved the lives of thousands of infants. The long heating kills the germs of consumption, typhoid fever, diphtheria, scarlet fever, and diarrhœa without destroying the good qualities of the milk, at least to any serious extent. Until such times, therefore, as milk dealers in cities and towns supply milk that is graded upon some standard of cleanliness under the supervision of the Board of Health, we should either buy properly pasteurized milk or pasteurize it for ourselves.

In pasteurizing milk care should be taken that it is not boiled. Boiling milk several times at intervals will sterilize it, but boiling changes the qualities of the milk, makes it hard to digest, and frequently causes constipation.

---

## CHAPTER XXX

### MILK AND DISEASE

Milk may be the means of spreading disease through a village, town, or city, if the germs of disease have been sown in it. No one knows how many different kinds of disease may thus be carried from house to house in milk; but we do know that consumption, typhoid fever, scarlet fever, diphtheria, and diarrhœa are spread in this way. Of course, these diseases are not thus spread over a country district, because milk is not peddled from one farmhouse to another; but, every doctor knows how disease may be spread from house to house along the route of a milkman.

Perhaps I can best make this clear by giving you a brief account of how an outbreak of scarlet fever took place in Norwalk, Conn., in November, 1897. This city has a population of 22,000, and is supplied with milk by seven or eight dealers. The outbreak was sudden, no fewer than 29 cases occurring between October 25th and November 9th. Before this there had been a few cases:

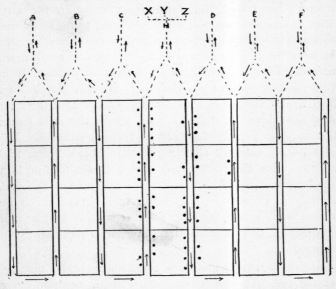

FIGURE 70.—Diagram to illustrate the route of Mr. H., the milk-driver, along the streets of Norwalk. The black dots represent scarlet fever cases. The letters A, B, C, H, D, E, F are intended to represent the depôts of the milk dealers. The letters X, Y, Z represent the homes of the three farmers from whom H. obtained his milk.

for example, in August, 0 cases; in September, 5 cases; on October 10th, only 1 case. What was the cause of the sudden increase in cases up to 29 in about two weeks?

In investigating the outbreak the first thing which the medical health officer did was to find out all the houses in which there were scarlet fever cases, and ask the inmates where they obtained their milk. He found that 27 of the 29 householders bought milk from one dealer, whom we shall call Mr. H. The milk supply to the city was supposed to be about 3,500 quarts, of which Mr. H. supplied about 450 quarts, or about $\frac{1}{8}$th of the whole. Yet he had, along his milk route, $\frac{27}{29}$ths of all the scarlet fever cases in the city. This looked very suspicious, so the next thing to do was to find out whether there were any cases of fever in Mr. H.'s family. None were found. Mr. H. was not himself a farmer ; he bought the milk which he peddled from three farmers, whom we shall call Mr. X., Mr. Y., and Mr. Z. So the medical health officer saw that the next step was to visit the farms from which the milk came. On doing so, he found no scarlet fever at either Mr. Y's or Mr. Z.'s ; but got clear proof that Mr. X.'s son had had the fever, the scarlet rash having broken out on him on October 24th. As the son was only four years of age, it can readily be seen that, after nursing the child, the germs would pass to the milk from the hands and clothing of the father and mother, who did their own milking.

As an illustration of how milk may spread disease, let me tell you about an outbreak of typhoid fever that occurred in Elkton, Maryland, in 1900. This town had a population of 2,542, and was supplied with milk from four dairy farms, which we shall speak of as Mr. A.'s, Mr. B.'s, Mr. C.'s, and Mr. D.'s. The total number of cases of typhoid which occurred in this outbreak was 64, and the patients all resided in 39 different houses. All of the 39 different houses obtained their milk from dairyman Mr. B.—a very suspicious circumstance. But, you will at once say: "Perhaps the typhoid came from the water which these families used and not from Mr. B.'s milk." Water is, of course, always a probable source of infection. Investigation of the water-supply, however, showed that 21 of the 39 householders used the town water-supply from the Elk river; and that the

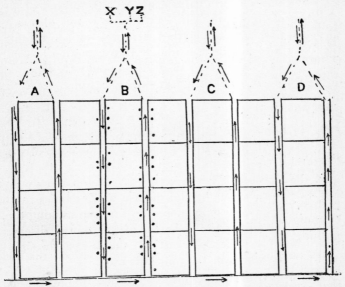

FIGURE 71.—Diagram to illustrate the route of Mr. B., the milk-driver, along the streets of Elkton. The black dots represent typhoid fever cases. Other references as in Figure 70.

other 18 householders used water from private wells. Clearly, therefore, the water-supply was not the source of the infection.

There were no typhoid cases along the milk routes of the other three milk dealers. On tracing the milk back to its source, the medical health officer found that dairy-farmer Mr. B. peddled not only the milk from his own farm, but also that from two other farmers whom we shall name Mr. X. and Mr. Y. Inquiry showed that there had been no cases of typhoid at either of these two farms, but that Mrs. B. had assisted in nursing a case of typhoid at an adjoining farmhouse, Z., for two or three weeks up to October 5th. Please note carefully the following dates. On October 8th, Mrs. B. and one of her sons became too ill to work. Previously to this, although they had both been ailing, they were well enough to milk the cows and handle the milk. Later, another son fell sick. On October 11th, 3 cases of typhoid were reported in the town ; on the 12th, 1 more case ; on the 13th, 2 others ; on the 14th, 3 others ; on the 15th, 3 more ; on the 16th, 3 more ; on the 18th, 6 more ; and by the 28th, 32 families in all had typhoid fever among their members. All used Mr. B.'s milk. At this date, Mr. B. discontinued selling milk, and in three weeks the outbreak had ceased. There seems no reasonable doubt that the mother caught the disease at Z.'s house and gave it to her two sons at home, and that in milking the cows and handling the milk the germs of the disease passed into the milk and scattered the disease throughout the town wherever the milk was used.

One or two events occurred in connection with this outbreak which are well worth noting, as showing how typhoid in one locality may be transferred to another distant one. Miss M., living in New Jersey, visited Elkton for two days, October 5th and 6th, returning home on the 7th. On the 14th she fell ill with typhoid. While in Elkton, she had drunk milk which had come from Mr. B.'s farm. So far as known, she had not been exposed to any other source of infection.

In another case, a negro servant, whose chief food was oatmeal porridge and milk, left Elkton about the middle of October and went to Glasgow, Delaware. There she became ill with typhoid fever and died.

In a third case, the married daughter of a resident of Elkton, left the town the 31st of October, to visit friends

FIGURE 72.—Cleaning cows before milking.

at a distance. In about ten days she was down with the disease, though there had been no cases in her father's family. The milk used in these two last cases was Mr. B.'s.

To impress upon you still further the certainty that milk carries disease, let me give you the bare facts about an outbreak of another disease, diphtheria, which occurred in three adjoining towns, Dorchester, Milton, and Hyde Park, Massachusetts, in 1907.

On April 12th, after a period of comparative freedom from this disease, 1 case of it was reported in Milton; on the 13th, 11 new cases were reported; on the 14th, 1 additional case; on the 15th, 4 other cases; on the 16th, 1 other case; in all 18 cases.

In Dorchester, the outbreak occurred as follows: on April 12th, 6 cases; on the 13th, 19 new cases; and on the 14th, 11 more cases.

In Hyde Park, the number of cases and dates were as follows: April 13th, 2 cases; 14th, 5 new cases; 15th, 6 more cases; 16th, 1 case; 17th, 3 cases; and 19th, 1 case.

Careful inquiry by the medical health officer showed that all the cases in Milton and Dorchester obtained their milk from one dairyman whom we shall call Mr. A.; while all the cases in Hyde Park obtained theirs from Mr. B. On tracing the milk supply back to its source, it was found that it all came from six farms. Clearly, the next step was to find out if there had been any diphtheria among the people living on these farms. It was soon discovered that on one farm a child had been seized with this disease on April 11th. The cooler in which the milk was mixed on this farm was washed in the farmhouse by the person who had nursed the sick child. The farmer sold about one-third of his milk to dairyman Mr. B., who peddled it through Hyde Park, and the rest of it to dairyman Mr. A., who delivered it to his customers in Dorchester and Milton.

There is a kind of consumption found among cows which is very much like that which attacks human beings. It is called "bovine" consumption. When cows have suffered for some time from this disease, it spreads to the udder, and the germs are found in the milk. Whether the flesh of tuberculous cows will give human beings consumption or not is a matter in dispute; but we do know that the milk from such cows produces

FIGURE 73.—A clean well-lighted, well-ventilated cow-stable.

bovine tuberculosis in weak and sickly people, and especially in infants.

It has been discovered that sometimes half the cows which supply milk to a town or city are tuberculous, but as a rule, not more than five per cent. of the cows in Canada or the United States are thus affected. In some places large numbers of such animals have been slaughtered in order to protect the public health; but recently the slaughter has been largely discontinued on account of the heavy loss which falls upon the owners.

The conviction is growing every day that, if we would decrease the spread of this disease among cattle, we must see to it that the stables in which they live are properly constructed. Cow stables should be large enough in proportion to the number of the herd to give every animal ample air space and plenty of light; the food should be plentiful and of the best quality; the building should be kept scrupulously clean; and when an animal is losing flesh, coughing frequently, or giving other signs of being unwell, it should be isolated from the rest of the herd.

Until such times as farmers erect better stables, keep them cleaner, feed their cows better, and see that the animals get plenty of sunshine and fresh air both winter and summer, just so long will their herds suffer from bovine consumption and be a menace to people who drink the milk.

## CHAPTER XXXI

### CONSUMPTION, OR TUBERCULOSIS

Tuberculosis was known to Hippocrates, a Greek physician, nearly five hundred years before Christ. "Phthisis," he says, "is the greatest and most cruel disease, and one that kills the greatest number of people." It is probable that phthisis was one of the diseases which were prevalent among the Israelites and that it is referred to in Deuteronomy under the terms pestilence and consumption; "The Lord shall make the pestilence cleave unto thee, until He shall have consumed thee from off the land. . . . The Lord shall smite thee with a consumption, and with a fever, and with an inflammation, and with an extreme burning."

The Greek name of the disease, phthisis, and the English one, consumption, indicate its prominent symptom—the wasting away of the body.

Preceding chapters have indicated clearly enough that the disease is due to a parasitic plant known as the "tubercle bacillus." Tuberculosis, the newer name of

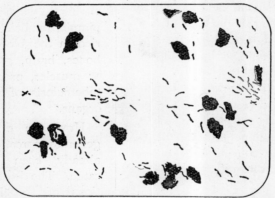

FIGURE 74.—The small dark curved lines denote the germs of tuberculosis, known as tubercle bacilli. The large black irregularly rounded figures are minute pieces of lung.

the disease, has been given to it because the bacilli accumulate in different parts of the body in little lumps, or tubercles, as they are generally called. These tubercles consist of immense numbers of the bacilli crowded into a part of some organ of the body and surrounded by a covering of what resembles white tough skin. So long as the bacilli are retained in this covering they are harmless, and after some time they die if the patient's strength keeps up. If not, they escape and infect other parts of the body and finally cause death.

The bacillus plant generally enters the body with the air we breathe, lodges in the lungs, and produces pulmonary,

or lung, tuberculosis. Less frequently it enters the stomach with the food and produces intestinal tuberculosis. Still less frequently it enters the body through a scratch or pimple, and being carried in the blood to bones, brain, glands, or muscles, produces tuberculosis of these organs.

How the disease generally spreads has already been indicated. The dead portions of the lungs which are coughed up from time to time

FIGURE 75.—One way in which the germs of consumption are spread in dust.

and known as "sputa," are a fruitful source of infection.

Saliva is the healthy juice which flows into the mouth from the salivary glands. Sputum, on the other hand, means the mixture of saliva and dead matter from the throat or lungs which is discharged after a single cough, or an attack of coughing. Sputa is the plural of sputum and signifies the diseased material that is coughed up during a period of time.

When tuberculosis sputum dries upon a floor or side-walk and becomes ground into powder by the trampling of many feet, thousands of the tiny plants float as fine dust in the air and enter the lungs of healthy people. This is the reason you will see notices posted up forbidding people to spit upon the floors of public buildings or upon the side-walks.

Now, while this is no doubt one common way in which the disease is spread, it is not by any means the only way. A consumptive mother may give the disease to her child by kissing it. Or a consumptive person may cough over the food at the family table and give the disease to others ; for, in coughing, it often happens that very fine particles of froth or spittle are ejected from the mouth. These may contain the germs of consumption, and falling upon the food, they may enter the stomach of another person and give him the disease.

Then, again, the dishes, knives, forks, spoons, towels, and clothing of a consumptive may be the means of carrying the germs to others. For some of the sputa or other discharges may accidentally fall upon some of these articles and the germs be thus conveyed to others.

There are two effectual means of preventing the spread of consumption. One is to kill, if possible, every germ that leaves the body of a consumptive, and the other way is to keep ourselves well and strong. The germ is dangerous only to persons who are in a run down condition of health. A man or woman, a boy or girl, is immune while strong and vigorous. But when one is suffering from a severe cold, or when just recovering from an attack of la grippe, measles, scarlet fever, or any other disease, then is the time to be on one's guard. Drunkenness, overwork, worry, too little rest or sleep, too little food, ill-digested food, a dusty atmosphere, bad ventilation, foul odours from sewage, —anything and everything in fact which will lower the vitality of the body renders us liable to take consumption when we are exposed to the germs

So wide-spread are the germs and so general are the causes which render people liable to take the disease, that a very large proportion of the population of this continent over eighteen years of age either have the disease now or have had it

While the disease is thus very prevalent not only in America but all over the world, we must not lose sight of the fact that it is largely preventable ; that is, the vast majority of those who are suffering from it need never have taken it. Not that the time will ever come when there will be no tuberculosis in the world. No doubt this disease will exist as long as the world lasts. When we speak of its being preventable, we mean that just as the deaths from small-pox, diphtheria, and typhoid fever have been greatly reduced of late years, so the deaths from tuberculosis may be very largely reduced if people will only take the trouble to fight it.

Another important fact to remember is that, in its early stages, consumption is curable ; in the advanced stages, it is not. The idea that it is curable is comparatively recent. Forty years ago the general opinion was that it was hereditary and incurable. People then believed that if either parent died of the disease, some one or more of the children were sure to die of it. To-day, however, all competent physicians believe that it is not hereditary. And they know too that, if they can recognize tuberculosis of the lungs in time, they can give their patients such treatment as will enable most of them to recover within a few years.

While it may be definitely stated that tuberculosis is not hereditary, there is no doubt that some families are naturally more liable than others to take it. This may be because such families inherit a poor quality of blood, or because those parts of the body are weak which the germs usually attack. The predisposition, as it is called, to take the disease is probably no greater than a predisposition to heart disease or kidney disease in other families.

When we learn, therefore, that parents and relatives of ours have died of tuberculosis or any other disease, the fact need not depress us. We can comfort ourselves with the assurance that we shall not necessarily die of the family weakness ; that, if we live sane, healthful, regular lives, we stand a very good chance of living out the allotted span of life notwithstanding our inherited disadvantage.

Between 150,000 and 200,000 die of this disease every year in the United States and Canada. This is a most appalling fact. It means that in one year as many persons die in North America of this disease as were killed in the earthquake in southern Italy in 1908. It means that, if all the school children in the Province of Nova Scotia should die next year, their deaths would number little more than half of the deaths which result from tuberculosis : it means that a number equal to the whole school population of Ontario would disappear in two and a half years. Or to put the facts in another way, it means that about 20 persons die of it every hour or 500 every day.

Now it is morally certain that for one who dies of this disease there are at least three who are suffering from it.

In other words, there must be to-day about 500,000 people in North America who require treatment for this disease. How can they be cared for? Not in hospitals nor sanatoria, because there is not sufficient accommodation for this number in all the hospitals in America, even if they were used entirely for this class of patients. Most of these cases must, therefore, be treated at home and by the family physician. Hence, care should be taken that all new houses are sanitary, and that unsanitary houses should be torn down or altered and sanitary ones built in their stead.

## CHAPTER XXXII

### CONSUMPTION AND THE HOME

Consumption is largely confined to human dwellings and is therefore spoken of as a house disease. Treat-

FIGURE 76.—Plan for a cheap sanitary cottage, designed for a working-man's family by Dr. Carrington, the Assistant Secretary of the United States National Association for the Study and Prevention of Tuberculosis.

ment in the home being unavoidable, what rules should be followed so as to prevent the disease spreading from one member of a family to another?

Keeping in mind the fact that the tubercle bacilli are usually spread from sputa or from small particles of

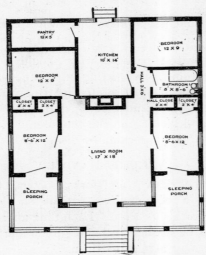

FIGURE 77.—Floor plans of Dr. Carrington's house. Note the sleeping porches upon which the tuberculous, or other members of the family, may sleep throughout the year.

sputum ejected in coughing and sneezing, boys and girls will easily understand the reasons for the following rules :—

## SPUTUM

1. Consumptives should deposit all sputum in a spittoon containing a strong germicide, such as a 5% solution of carbolic acid in water.

2. If sputum is deposited in a handkerchief, it should not be allowed to dry, but the handkerchief should be boiled for half an hour and then washed.

3. A consumptive, when out of his room, should use a pocket spittoon, and this should be regularly disinfected.

4. He should always, when coughing, hold a clean cloth over his mouth. This cloth should afterwards be burnt.

5. He should not swallow his own sputum, because by doing so he may take consumption of the intestines.

6. The greatest possible care should be taken to prevent sputum from getting upon the hands, face, clothing, or bed-clothes of the patient himself or of others who may wait upon him. If this should happen, the hands and face should be thoroughly cleansed and the articles of clothing carefully disinfected.

## Articles Handled

1. All dishes, knives and forks, spoons, etc., used or handled by a consumptive patient should be kept exclusively for his own use. Each time after being used they should be washed in boiling-hot water to kill any germs that may adhere to them.

2. Consumptives should not be assigned to any situation or carry on any occupation in which they would be required to handle food or clothing belonging to other people.

3. The wearing apparel of consumptives should be disinfected if it is to be used by others.

## Rooms

1. The rooms occupied by consumptives should not have carpets or contain anything which will harbour dust particles. Rugs and curtains should never be shaken, beaten, or swept, except in the open air and after being exposed to sunlight for a few hours. Shaking or beating rugs and curtains will scatter the

germs through the air and thus become a means of spreading the disease. Bed-clothes should be frequently exposed to sunlight.

2. Damp cloths should be used in dusting floors, wood-work, furniture, windows, and walls, and these cloths should be afterwards well boiled.

3. Bedroom windows should be open night and day, summer and winter.

4. A consumptive should not sleep in the same bed as another person. If possible, each patient should have a room to himself.

5. When a consumptive vacates a room, it should be thoroughly disinfected. Its wall-paper, if any, should be removed, and then the floors, woodwork, windows, walls, and ceiling thoroughly washed with a disinfecting solution or sterilized with formaldehyde vapour. Afterwards, as much air and sunlight as possible should be admitted.

### Conduct

1. Consumptives should not kiss other people.

2. They should spend most of the time in the open air.

3. In the early stages of the disease they should occupy themselves in some light labour for a short time each day.

If a consumptive carefully observes all these rules relating to sputum, articles handled, and care of room, he may live in a home for months without communicating the disease to others.

It is impossible to give adequate directions in this book for the treatment of tuberculosis ; but, in order to show the importance which is attached to diet, sunshine and fresh air, let me give you the daily routine of one of our Canadian sanatoria :—

At a quarter-past seven the rising bell rings, after which each patient who is able, is expected to take a cold bath.

Breakfast follows, consisting of fruit, a cereal, meat and potatoes, coffee, or cocoa.

Then comes the distribution of fresh sputum cups and of clean dust-cloths. Each girl, unless excused by the physician, has to keep her own room in order. Outside of each room is a supply of carbolic acid solution. Dust-cloths are saturated with this, and the floor and each article of furniture in the room is "carbolized," that is, dusted off with carbolic solution. Of course there is no carpet on the floor and the furniture is simple : iron bedstead, rocking-chair, small table and dresser.

The rooms must be done up in twenty minutes, and then forty minutes are spent sitting out on the verandah.

At 10.30, "diets" are served. These consist of eggs, milk, scraped beef, or whatever else the doctor may order for the building up of the patient.

At 12.40, comes the call for dinner. Dinner consists of soup, two kinds of meat, two kinds of vegetables, dessert, and milk.

At 3.30, "diets" are again served.

At 5.40, patients get ready for supper, and after supper they may do as they please.

At 9.30, there are "diets" for the third time.

Each patient has six meals a day, and spends eight hours a day in the open air.

Eggs play a very large part in the "diets" and in the other meals of the patients. Sometimes a patient lives exclusively on eggs, taking the whites of as many as forty eggs each day.

Many methods are used for entertaining the patients, because recreation is as necessary as medicine. There is a library for those inclined to read, though reading must not interfere with their eight hours out of doors. There are billiards and pool ; and there is a stage where entertainments are presented by the children and young women. Many of the patients have gardens for themselves, and raise two crops from them, an early one of lettuce and radishes, a second of flowers. There are also playrooms for the girls and boys on rainy days.

While the observance of this routine, together with sleeping outside, both summer and winter, will greatly aid in recovery, there are several other things about which a patient needs the special instruction of a physician, and any of you who may have the disease will do well to consult the family doctor from time to time as may seem necessary.

Very frequently in the past, physicians have advised consumptives to remove from the colder parts of America to the warmer. This practice is being largely abandoned. The fact is, that people who have been born and brought up in a cold climate and who are suffering from this disease, make better progress toward recovery by remaining in the North than by going South. A cool, dry, elevated, equable climate is the best. The cool air seems to check the disease ; the warm air either favours it or, at least, does not restrain its progress.

Careful observations point to the conclusion that, as an aid to recovery, one winter is as good as three summers, at least to those who have been accustomed to a cool climate.

---

## CHAPTER XXXIII

### THE CHOICE OF A DWELLING

What sort of house should we live in ? Should it be large or small ? Should it be built of stone, brick, wood, or concrete ? Should it be located upon a hill or in a hollow ? If in a city should the presence of dust and smoke be carefully considered ? Should a low rental be the chief consideration or should the house be chosen because it is sanitary ; that is, because it will help to conserve the health and well-being of the family ?

It would be waste of time to discuss with you the requisites of a large modern house—its site, foundation, size, lighting, heating, furniture, and materials of construction. Such houses are only for the few. Rather let us consider what the minimum requirements should be in a house for a labouring man and his family. And first of all, should the house be large or small?

Before you attempt to answer this question, let me ask you to consider some statistics that were collected by the late Dr. J. B. Russell, medical health officer of Glasgow, Scotland :—

| Size of House. | Number of people living in these houses. | Percentage of total population. | Percentage of total number of deaths. | Deaths per year. |
|---|---|---|---|---|
| One room . . . . | 134,728 | 24.7 | 27.0 | 3,636 |
| Two rooms . . . . | 243,691 | 44.7 | 47.0 | 6,325 |
| Three rooms . . . . | 86,956 | 16.0 | 13.0 | 1,747 |
| Four rooms . . . . | 32,742 | 6.1 | 4.3 | 581 |
| Five rooms and upward | 38,647 | 7.1 | 3.3 | 434 |
| Public Institutions . | 6,531 | 1.4 | 3.2 | 427 |
| Untraced . . . . . | | | 2.2 | 289 |
| Whole city population | 543,295 | 100 | 100 | 13,439 |

Now turn back to Chapter IV and look at the three diagrams which illustrate the relation between the size of dwelling-houses and the diseases that afflict the inmates. Then note the high death-rate, as given above, among people who live in homes of one or two rooms. These rooms must be used as kitchen, living room, bedroom, washroom, and bathroom, and so must help to cause the high death-rate unless they are kept scrupulously clean and well ventilated.

As you may see, about half the inhabitants of Glasgow live in two-room houses. The percentage of deaths in these houses is higher than the percentage of population.

In some other cities in Europe the conditions are quite as bad as in Glasgow.   In American cities, while the conditions are somewhat better, it is nevertheless true that just in proportion as people crowd together in cities, so there is a corresponding increase in the death-rate.

Note again the much lower death-rate—only 3.3 per cent.—among the inmates of those homes which have five rooms and upwards.   So low is the death-rate here that you are, no doubt, quite prepared to say at once that no family should ever live in a house that contains less than five rooms.   As there is an average of about five persons in every family, it follows that the death-rate is lowest in homes in which there is an average of one room for each member of the family.

Perhaps some of you may tell me that it must make a great difference whether the five rooms are small or large. So it will.   You can easily imagine a family living in a five-roomed house, in which the rooms are so small that they do not contain as much air as does many a one-roomed or two-roomed house.   A house, for example, such as many of the early settlers in America built, had only two rooms—one on the ground floor and one up-stairs, and yet in these two-room homes the death-rate was very low.   One reason for this was that only the strong and hardy emigrated to the New World.   Another reason was that the heating and cooking were done by means of large, open fireplaces, and consequently the ventilation was unusually good.

Accordingly, we cannot decide upon the proper size of a house simply by counting its rooms.   We must look at their size as well.

If possible we must fix upon the number of cubic feet of air that each member of a family should have, in

order that his health may not suffer from lack of oxygen.
Suppose we fix upon the air space which has been prescribed by law for schools as a fair standard for adults
as well as for children. This standard is different in
different localities. In Ontario it is 1,000 cubic feet per
hour for each child, but in many places in the United
States it is 2,000 cubic feet. Applying the lower standard
to a labouring man's house, we find that if there are
five persons in it, the house should contain a space of at
least 5,000 cubic feet. This would mean a house about
25 feet long, 20 feet wide, and 10 feet high, whether it
contained one room or five. On the higher standard of
2,000 cubic feet per person, the house would require to
be double the number of cubic feet given above.

A house of smaller size than 25 feet long, 20 feet
wide, and 10 feet high, would do for a family of five, if
its ventilation were so perfect that the amount of carbon
dioxide in the air could be kept down to the standard of
$\frac{2}{25}$ths of one per cent. This standard, however, cannot
be maintained in small houses without creating a draught
that might be dangerous to the health of the inmates. In
fact, one reason why so many houses are badly ventilated
is because the inmates object to draughts. It is agreed
among physiologists that the volume of air that must
enter a house in order to keep the air fresh, and at the
same time without producing an objectionable draught
is 1,000 cubic feet per hour per person.

Having fixed upon the minimum size—and no family
however poor should live in a smaller one—let us consider some of the other requisites of a sanitary house.

The windows should be large in proportion to the size
of the house, so that sunshine may flood every room,

killing microbes and aiding in the production of good red blood in those inmates who are compelled to live all day in the house. The window frames should be so constructed as to allow the upper portions to be transoms turning on a pivot and thus promoting ventilation. As a further aid toward adequate ventilation, outlet air-ducts (as already described on page 20) should lead from each room to a large air-flue in the chimney or adjoining it.

The bedrooms should open upon sleeping porches by means of either French windows or Dutch doors. The former are really glass doors which open down to the level of the floor. The Dutch door consists of an upper half which is exactly like a window, and may be raised by pulleys and weights so as to disappear into the wall above. The lower half is like an ordinary door, being hinged to open inward or outward.

The purpose of both the French window and the Dutch door is to aid in ventilation, and to allow the bed to be rolled out upon the verandah or sleeping porch and to be withdrawn at pleasure.

Every consumptive at least, and in fact other members of the family also, would be benefited by sleeping on the porches throughout the year. On the approach of winter the beds should be withdrawn from the sleeping porches during the day into a warm bedroom. After preparing for bed in the warm room, the bed should be rolled out on to the sleeping porch and should remain there all night. Of course the bed-clothes must be adequate. The head also must be protected with a cap warm enough to prevent the sleeper from catching cold. In the morning the occupant returns to the warm bedroom, where the dressing is done.

In summer additional sleeping accommodation may be afforded by a flat roof on the house, where, by the use of screens, each member of a family may have practically a private compartment to himself. Of course there would have to be canvas overhead to protect the beds in rainy weather.

The success which has attended the open-air treatment of consumption indicates clearly enough that, if a man would protect his family from this disease, he must seek a house that is provided with either sleeping porches or the most perfect kind of ventilation.

FIGURE 78.—Mr. Milton Dana Morrill's plan for a five-room concrete house. Awarded the gold medal by the International Congress concerning Tuberculosis, Washington, D.C., 1908. Houses for working-men have been erected in accordance with these plans for $1,000 each.

The site of a dwelling should be chosen so as to secure pure air, plenty of sunshine, and perfect drainage. If, in addition, we can have good neighbours, and attractive natural surroundings we shall be fortunate indeed.

As regards the foundation, many houses are too low. Generally speaking, the earth which comes out of the cellar should be graded round the house, so as to form a terrace about eighteen inches above the natural level of

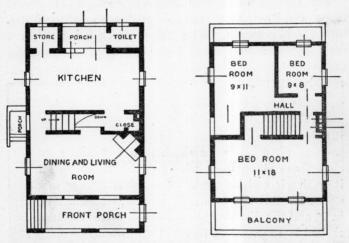

FIGURE 79.—Floor plans of Mr. Morrill's house.   Note the sleeping balcony in front and the one behind.  Upon these, tuberculous or other members of a family may sleep throughout the year.

the ground.   The first floor should be at an elevation of about two or three feet above this grading.   When this is the case, the basement need not be dug much below the surface level—a most important matter in securing good drainage in a flat district.

The materials out of which houses are usually built are brick, stone, wood, or concrete.   It would be useless for us to discuss the comparative advantages and disadvantages of each of these.   No one doubts that a perfectly sanitary house can be built out of any one of them; but whether houses with soft-wood floors, baseboards, wooden doors and window frames can be kept hygienic without a great deal of trouble and labour is open to doubt.

To be sanitary a house should be provided in summer with screens on the doors and windows for the purpose of keeping out house-flies. These insects are to be found everywhere in the northern parts of North America in July, August, and September. As scavengers they visit privy-vaults, decaying flesh and all kinds of dead waste from animals. If windows and doors are not screened, they are likely to visit the table during meal-time, and in walking over the food may transfer the germs of disease to members of the family.

As food must be kept fresh in order to be wholesome, it follows that every sanitary house should be provided with a cold-air closet in which food can be kept. This closet should be lined with galvanized iron. Through it fresh air can be made to circulate during moderate and cold weather. In hot weather, ice must be used in it, and the dirt that always accumulates in an ice-box should be removed by flushing with water.

In cities, a house generally has its waste-pipes connected with the kitchen-sink, bathroom, and water-closet. It is of the utmost importance, therefore, that the joints of the drain-pipes, and all traps which open into them should be so tight that not the least trace of any bad odour can be found in the house. In fact, the drainage of a house must be carefully considered in every detail ; all the more so, if the house is located in a flat district, where there can be little or no fall of the ground away from the house.

The furnishings of a house should be such as to throw as little labour as possible upon the housekeeper.

When floors are buried under carpets, when windows are hidden with lace curtains, and walls are covered with paper, it is very difficult to keep a house clean, and a dirty house is an unsanitary house. Painted walls are even more sanitary than whitewashed ones, because they can be readily washed; and, similarly, painted floors are more sanitary than bare ones.

The greatest care should be taken to furnish a house simply. Hardwood chairs and tables are all that are necessary for the kitchen and living room. Single iron bedsteads should be the rule. Folding beds or sofa-beds are objectionable on hygienic grounds. Generally they are used to save space, and in the morning are closed up too soon to allow of the bed-clothes being properly aired and sunned; but, with sleeping porches in general use as they should be, there would be no necessity for using folding beds.

Some of you are no doubt asking whether the fore-going requirements for a labouring-man's house are not too high. Before deciding this question, read over again the chapter on the effects of bad air, look again at the tables which show the effects of living in small, sunless, and badly ventilated houses, note the small size and the lack of ventilation in the houses of many working-men, and then say whether in your opinion there are not to-day too many of these houses which entail upon their inmates the certainty of sickness and untimely death.

A house which will not promote the health of every one of its inmates should be either altered or pulled down.

Lastly, I hope the time may soon come when a sanitary history shall be kept of every dwelling-house in each municipality. This history should be written by the medical health officer and preserved among the municipal records, so that it can be consulted by any person who intends to live in the house. " What an unreasonable thing ! " you say. Not unreasonable at all, but sober common sense ; because nearly every doctor can give instances of how small-pox, measles, scarlet fever, and particularly consumption, have been communicated to people who have moved into infected houses.

Let me quote an instance of this from the records of the department of health for Pennsylvania. Between 1889 and 1901, a family of six, consisting of father and mother and four children, occupied a farmhouse in this state, and during these years four died of consumption. In 1902-03, another family, two parents and eight children, occupied the same house but soon moved out of it on account of illness, the father and one child suffering from the disease. In 1904, the house again became occupied by a father, mother, and eight children. Of these, three have well developed signs of consumption and three others are suspected to be infected with it. In 1905, the house became occupied by two parents and two children, the father being a son of the man who occupied it in 1889. This man has since died of the disease.

Summing up the record of this plague-smitten house, we find that there have been in all fourteen cases. Surely you will agree with me that if a sanitary history had been kept of it, people would not have rented it ; or if they did, they would at least have learned beforehand from the Medical Health Officer that they were running great risks of taking the disease, and would have had it thoroughly disinfected.

## CHAPTER XXXIV

### GENERAL WORK OF THE NERVOUS SYSTEM

If you have been working very hard at any kind of manual labour or playing any very active game like football or hockey, you have often become much more tired than you were at first aware of.   Or, again, you may have gone for a long tramp on snow-shoes, and have come back so wearied that you could hardly drag one foot after the other.   Most of you then, know very well what it is to have very tired muscles.   But you may not know that it is the nerves which make the muscles work, and that you can not tire out your muscles without at the same time tiring your nerves.

When you are working hard at any manual labour, you can rest in a measure by simply standing still for a while.   You can rest still better by sitting down ; you can rest best of all by lying down.   This is the way in which the heart is rested.   You know the heart is just a muscle or a bundle of muscles.   Get some one to count your pulse-beats, that is your heart-beats, when you are standing ; then sit down and have them counted a second time, and you will find that the beats are fewer ; lie down, and have them counted a third time, and you will now find that they are still fewer than when you were sitting. This is the only way in which the heart muscle gets any rest.   The muscles used in breathing also rest in the same way as the heart muscle rests.   In the case of many other muscles of your body, it is different.   Those of your arms and legs work only when you make them work.   They rest when you sit down or lie down; whereas the heart muscle works night and day as long as you live.

We need not wonder, then, that all the muscles of our body become tired and need rest. But what about nerves? Do they also need rest, or can they go on all day without getting tired? Think a little and you will see that the nerves do a great deal of work. Those of the skin tell us when we are hurt, or cut, or are too hot, or too cold. The nerves of the teeth tell us, of course, when they are worried by a decayed tooth. And the nerves of the mouth tell us all about our food at meal-times,—and often between meals. They tell us also that candy is sweet, and that some medicines are nasty. If we go into a dirty school-room or a musty church, the nerves of the nose tell us that these places have a bad smell, and warn us to get out again into the fresh air. In a saw-mill or machine-shop the nerves of the ear become tired by the noise, and, when we try to converse in such places, we have to shout so loud that it is very tiresome. So too, when you have been in school all day, reading, writing, and ciphering, your eyes become tired. Some of your muscles also become tired, and almost without knowing why, you have a great longing to get away out of school and see something else than its four walls, and tiresome blackboard.

The fact is that a vast number of nerves, like fine white threads, run from the eye, ear, nose, mouth, skin, muscles, and joints, and are carrying messages to the brain and spinal cord every second of the day. Is it any wonder, then, that these nerves become tired carrying messages, and that the brain and spinal cord get tired receiving these messages? But to receive messages is not the only work of the brain. Many of the messages have to be stored away for future use. When you were made to learn the letters of the alphabet, the names and meanings of a vast number of words, tables of numbers, facts of history and geography, and all the other thousand and one things which you have to learn in school— all these activities tired the nerves and brain.

Those of you who have taken a long journey in a railroad car will know how fatiguing it is.   Though you may have spent the day in a comfortable coach, you nevertheless reach the end of your journey pretty well tired out. The cause of your fatigue can not be due to the use of your muscles.   To what, then, is it due ?   Clearly, it has been caused by the vast number of messages which have crowded into the brain from the eye, ear, and muscles. Thousands of objects have passed before the eyes ; thousands of sounds have, one after another, fallen upon the ears ; the jolting and jarring of the car has sent thousands of messages from the muscles and joints; and it is little wonder that the nerves, spinal cord, and brain are thoroughly tired out at the end of the day's journey.

But besides receiving and storing messages the brain and spinal cord have all day long to be sending out messages as well.   Some of these we cause, but others are not under our control.   Those we cause begin to go out when we wake in the morning.   When we wish to wash and dress, stand, sit, walk, work, or play, not a muscle moves without an order from the brain or spinal cord.   Messages which we can not control are sent to the heart to change its beat from time to time.   Other messages vary the breathing.   And still others cause the saliva and other juices of the stomach, liver, and bowels to flow, so that the food will be digested and made fit to be used by the blood.

In short, the work of the nervous system is never done, from the time we awake in the morning until we go to sleep at night. No "central" office of any telephone company in the land is kept so busy as the brain is, in receiving, storing, and sending out messages. No wonder, then, that it becomes tired and needs rest. Moreover, fatigue comes on all the more quickly if our surroundings or other conditions are bad. If the air in our school-houses is bad, or the lighting bad, or the seats and desks too high or too low for the size of the pupils, or if children go to school with too little food or too little sleep, the fatigue comes on very soon in the forenoon, and the wonder is that such children can be taught anything under such conditions.

The brain and nerves do not, however, rest in the same way as muscles do. As I have already said, all you have to do in order to give muscles rest, is to sit or lie down. But this may not rest the brain at all. If the brain has been overworked, and worried during the day, as happens often with grown-up people and often with delicate children, then the brain does not begin to rest at all when they go to bed. It goes on worrying over the work or the events of the day ; and when this happens, it is often very late at night before the brain rests. If the worry is very great, sleep may not come at all.

Now, this is a very bad state for us to be in. It spoils our ability to use our brain. Even our muscles will not work as we wish, if we do not get enough sleep. If the worry lasts for some weeks or months, then we lose the power of digesting our food properly.

# CHAPTER XXXV

## THE STRUCTURE OF THE NERVOUS SYSTEM

As we have already seen the nervous system is the great governing power of every part of the body. It starts, controls, and stops all muscular movements; it determines whether glands shall secrete their juices or not; it regulates the flow of blood to the different parts as may be needed; it receives messages from, and sends out messages to, every part of the body; it gets from the eye, ear, skin, mouth, nose, and muscles information of objects and facts in the world around us; it stores these as memory; and it decides upon present and future conduct.

Not only, therefore, is the nervous system the governing power of the body, but it is also the seat of intelligence, will, and reason.

For convenience of description, it may be said to consist of three parts:

I. The brain, including (*a*) the cerebrum or large brain, and (*b*) the cerebellum or small brain. The cerebrum is partly divided into two halves, or hemispheres by a deep fissure which runs from front to back along its surface.

II. The bulb and the spinal cord, the latter being a large thick tube about the size of the forefinger, running from the cerebrum down the greater part of the length of the trunk, and inclosed for safety in the backbone. The bulb is the upper enlarged end of the cord where it joins the brain.

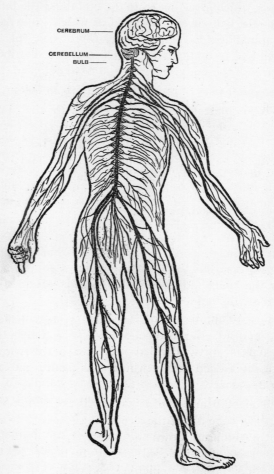

CEREBRUM

CEREBELLUM
BULB

FIGURE 80.—The Nervous System.

III. Twelve pair of nerves, or rather bundles of nerve-threads, which grow out from the brain and the bulb, and thirty-one pair of similar bundles which grow out from the spinal cord. These forty-three pair of nerves branch and re-branch very much, and are distributed to all parts of the body, internal and external.

The outer part of the brain is grayish in colour, and is, therefore, called the gray matter. The surface is marked with rounded ridges and fissures between them which vary in depth from one quarter of an inch to one inch. Below this gray matter, the brain substance consists of white matter, so called because the fibres or threads of which it is composed are white in colour, and very similar to the nerve-fibres in other parts of the body.

The fibres of the white matter are used either in receiving nerve messages from various parts of the body, or in transmitting messages from one part of the gray matter to another, or in sending messages from the brain out to muscles, glands, arteries, etc., in different regions of the body.

The nerve-fibres of the nervous system have often been likened to the separate wires of a telephone or telegraph cable. Just as each separate wire in a telephone cable can transmit a separate message, so each separate thread, or fibre, in a bundle of nerves carries its own message to or from the brain, or to or from the spinal cord.

By a study of certain diseases of the human brain as seen among patients in a hospital for the insane, and by experiments upon the brain of some of the lower animals, physiologists have discovered that certain

parts of the gray matter are connected with the special
senses,—sight, hearing, taste, touch and smell.

By similar methods of study it has been discovered
that the voluntary movements of the body are all
controlled from other areas of the gray matter. In
other words, the surface of each half of the brain
has been mapped out into areas, some of which are
concerned with receiving messages from the different

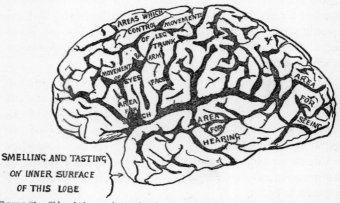

SMELLING AND TASTING
ON INNER SURFACE
OF THIS LOBE

FIGURE 81.—Side of the cerebrum showing areas connected with the senses or sensory
areas, and the areas connected with movement, that is, the "Motor Areas." The
dark lines denote the fissures in the gray matter.

senses, and others with sending out messages to the
muscles which control the voluntary movements of the
eyes, head, trunk, and limbs.

The areas which are concerned with voluntary movements, that is, the "motor areas," are, roughly speaking,
triangular in shape for each half of the brain. The bases
of each pair of triangles are upon the mid-line of the brain,
and the other two sides extend downwards to points
about half-way between the ear and the eye at each side.

From the gray matter of these areas, nerve-fibres extend down through the brain and run out along with the large nerves of the brain or spinal cord, ending finally in the voluntary muscles of the body. Every muscle is supplied with nerves which branch and re-branch throughout every part of it.

When we *will* to move any part of the body, the eyes, for example, messages start from the special area in the brain for movements of the eyes, pass downwards and out along three nerves which leave the brain, and, on reaching the eye muscles, produce contraction of these and consequently movement of the eyes in the direction in which we wish them to move.

Or, to take another example. In the case of the forearm; when we *will* or command the muscle to bend the elbow, the command passes as a message from the motor area of the brain down the upper part of the spinal cord, and out along a nerve to the arm. Branches of this nerve enter the biceps muscle, and, as a result of the nerve message reaching this muscle, it contracts and the arm is bent.

The proof of this connection of muscle and nerve is one of the great discoveries in physiology, and was well known over two hundred years ago.

It would appear from the foregoing that there are two different kinds of nerve-messages, or nerve-impulses, passing to and fro all the time throughout an animal's body. One set of messages are passing from the special sense organs, the skin and other parts of the body inwards to the spinal cord and brain; and a second set are passing from the brain, or spinal cord, outwards to muscles, glands, or other organs.

If we cut the nerve which carries an ingoing message, such a message never afterwards reaches the brain or cord, and we have loss of feeling known as "sensory paralysis." If we cut the nerve which carries an outgoing message, then such a message never afterwards reaches the muscle, it does not contract, and is, therefore, said to be paralyzed. A muscle that is cut off permanently from its nerve supply shrinks up and after some time loses its power of contraction.

The muscles of idiots are seldom, if ever, symmetrically developed, because the brain is not perfectly developed and therefore does not send out the nerve-impulses which alone will make the muscles grow. Such persons all walk, if they are able to walk at all, with an unsteady or shuffling gait.

On the other hand, amputation of the leg of an infant is followed by arrested development of certain parts of the brain. The parts affected in this case are the "motor areas" for movements of the leg and foot. If the eyes are destroyed, another part of the brain fails to develop properly, namely, the area for vision.

## CHAPTER XXXVI

### THE SENSE OF SIGHT

When we speak of the sense of sight, we are apt to think of it as depending on the eye only. In reality, however, the eye is only one part of the mechanism for seeing.

A study of the accompanying figure will show that this mechanism consists of three parts. There is first of all the eye, then there is the bundle of nerve-threads or fibres which run from the back part of the eye slightly upward into the floor of the brain, and then backward to the very hinder part of the cerebrum. These fibres constitute the second part of the mechanism of sight.

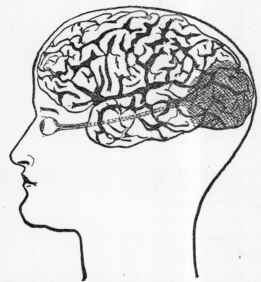

FIGURE 82.—Showing diagrammatically nerve-fibres from the eye to the area for sight.

The third part consists of the gray matter at the hinder part of the cerebrum in which the nerve-fibres end. This is the "area for sight."

If any one of these three parts becomes diseased, or damaged by accident, then the sense of sight becomes impaired or altogether lost.

It rarely happens that the nerve-threads which connect the eyeball with the cerebrum become severed. When they do, the person to whom such an accident happens goes blind, just the same as if he had had his eyes put out.

Equally rare is the case in which the hinder part of the cerebrum becomes injured or diseased; but, when this does occur, the person becomes blind in one or both eyes, the degree of blindness depending upon the extent of the injury or the extent of the diseased area. In such a case, a person may lose the power of recognizing words, and, may therefore, cease to be able to read. Eye memory, that is, the memory of things learned through the eye, becomes lost, and with this is lost much of the person's intelligence.

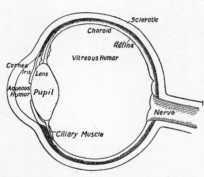

Figure 83.—Front to back section of the eye  The outer coat of the eye is the sclerotic; inside this is the choroid coat; the innermost one is the retina—the spread-out end of the optic nerve. The front covering of the eye is the cornea. The coloured part is the iris, and the circular opening in the iris is the pupil

Seeing, then, means that objects outside of us start messages from the back part of the eye, and that these travel along the nerve-fibres until they reach the area of the brain which is concerned in seeing. Here is stored the memory of all sights, places, and things which we have seen. In this part of the brain we learn to recognize printed and written words, and then to read. It is probably this area also that becomes highly trained in the artist, so that he can recognize subtle differences in light, shadow, colour, and form which untrained people can not see.

If the eye is not perfect, then a child's education may be delayed ; because wrong messages or imperfect messages may reach the area for sight and wrong impressions be formed in the child's mind. Hence, every child's eyes should be examined and his sight tested by the parent, the teacher, or a physician.

So much for the structure of the eye and its connection with the brain; now as to its care.

If you have headaches in school, often toward the noon hour or toward four o'clock in the afternoon, they are likely to be due to some trouble in the eyes. Of course, this is not always the case. The trouble may lie in some other part of the body ; but it is always safest, when troubles like these are noticed, to have a doctor examine the eyes and find out what is wrong.

You must be careful not to catch any disease of the eyes from other persons. There are some bad diseases of the eyes that may be caught by using water, towels, or handkerchiefs that diseased persons have used, or by touching some parts of a diseased person's body with your fingers and afterwards rubbing your eyes with them. These diseases are caused by germs, such as have been already described to you.

Have you ever heard of snow-blindness ? It comes upon people who have to travel a long distance over stretches of glistening snow, as when one crosses a northern prairie in winter. The same kind of trouble comes upon people who travel across the Sahara desert. The long stretches of white sand in Africa and of white snow in America, reflect the light so strongly into the eyes that after a while the nerve endings lose all power of doing their work and the traveller becomes temporarily or permanently blind.

It is part of the religion of a Mahommedan Arab not to shade his eyes in crossing the desert, and for  this reason as well as for lack of cleanliness, there is more eye disease among these Arabs than among other people. They do not wear caps or hats like ours, with peaks or brims on them which help the eyelids to keep out the painful glare of the sun ; consequently, the nerve of the eye is sometimes slowly killed by the intense light and at last blindness comes on.

FIGURE 84.—Arab's head. Eyes unshaded.

We should remember these facts, if we would avoid injuring the eyesight of babies. Very often a thoughtless mother may be seen pushing her baby along in its carriage and allowing the strong light of the sun to shine full into his eyes. This is very wrong. Of course, when the baby grows older and stronger, it will do no harm to have the sun shine into his eyes now and again ; but, when he is quite young, his eyes should always be shaded from very strong light, because the nerves of the eye are delicate and might be injured, just as those of a man's eye are sometimes injured in travelling over the snow or sand.

A steady, bright light is the best for reading or writing at night. Flickering unsteady lights, like those from candles, gas-jets, or arc lamps are trying to the eyes. Again, if you are too far away from a light, when you are reading at night and the print can not be clearly seen, almost without knowing it you bring the book close up to your eyes. This throws a double strain upon them, the cause of which you cannot understand just now ; but you may be quite sure that steady reading or doing fine work of any kind is bad for the eyes even in daytime, and very bad at night unless the light is bright and steady.

If you have sore eyes or weak ones, or have pain in them, or cannot see clearly to read, or cannot clearly see well-known things at a distance, then there is

FIGURE 85.—Baby's eyes should be properly shaded while out getting fresh air.

something wrong with your eyes, and you should go to a doctor and have them tested, so as to find out what the nature of the defect may be.

If you have always to hold a book nearer the face than twelve or fourteen inches, you are near-sighted and should wear glasses. If you have to hold the book farther away than seventeen or eighteen inches in reading it, you are far-sighted and need glasses and these should be procured as soon as possible, so as to relieve the "eye-strain" which must otherwise be the result.

## CHAPTER XXXVII

### HEARING, TASTE, AND SMELL

The part of the ear which we can see is not an essential part of the organ of hearing. Like the eye, the organ of hearing really consists of three parts. First, a part which can not be seen but which lies in one of the skull-bones at the side of the head; secondly, an area for hearing on the surface of the brain; and thirdly, a bundle of nerve-threads which join the first and second parts together. All three parts are necessary to perfect hearing.

We are apt to think that deafness is due to something going wrong with the ear or part of the outer organ. Quite often it is; but deafness may be due to something being wrong with the bundle of nerve-threads, or it may be due to a defect or injury in the area for hearing on the surface of the brain.

Figure 86 shows a brain that lacks at least part of this area, as shewn by the chasm or empty space on one side. The woman from whom this brain was taken was stone deaf all her life. When she was born, this part of the brain was lacking, and therefore no measure of education could ever have made her hear.

Hearing then requires much more than the possession of a perfect external ear. It is necessary that every sound which enters the ear should start messages which will travel along the nerve-threads until they reach the part of the brain concerned in hearing and be recorded there in our consciousness.

When the whistle sounds or the dinner horn is blown, the air carries the sound to the ears of the workers and they judge that a meal is ready. In the same way, the sound of the teacher's voice is carried through the air, enters the outer ear of the child, and, if his hearing is perfect, the message is carried into the brain by the nerve-threads of which I have spoken, and the brain area for hearing understands and stores up the teacher's instructions.

When we are young, the part of the brain concerned in hearing is being trained all the time, whether in

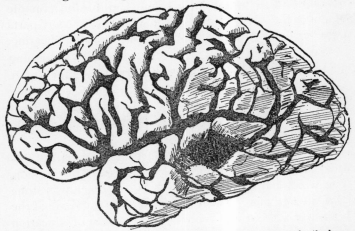

FIGURE 86.—Brain with part of the area for hearing lacking, as shown by the large dark spot.

school or out of school. By it we recognize the words that are spoken to us; by it we learn a piece of music and recognize familiar airs. If, therefore, a pupil learns his lessons very slowly and seems to be behind the rest of the class, the reason may be that he does not hear well, and, not hearing well, the information which the teacher gives him can not be readily stored in his brain.

What has been called the "auditory area" on the surface of the brain may not be storing sounds properly, because the pupil's outer ear is defective in form or structure. The outer organ and the brain part should work together, and they do work together when the mechanism of hearing is perfect; but, in some pupils who appear to be dull, these parts do not work together, and the result is dulness of understanding and backwardness in studies.

Of course, no small objects such as beans or peas should be put into the ear; nor should hard wax be allowed to remain in it. Accumulation of wax in the

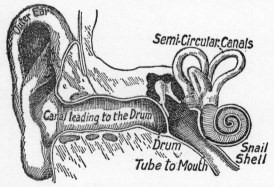

FIGURE 87.—External, Middle, and Inner parts of the Ear or Outer Organ of Hearing. The external part extends from left to right as far as the drum. The middle part comes next and is joined to the throat by a small tube, known as the Eustachian tube. The snail shell and semi-circular canals make up the inner part of the outer organ. The nerve of hearing joins the snail shell to the area for hearing.

outer ear impairs the hearing. It can usually be removed by gently syringing with warm water.

In caring for the ear, perhaps the most important thing is to avoid the effects of a severe cold. A prolonged cold in the throat should never be neglected; because the effect of the cold is to irritate the surface and make it a suitable soil upon which the germs of infectious disease may grow. From the throat, the disease may spread up the Eustachian tube into the ear, and, as a result, an abscess may form in the middle ear, and then there is danger of its spreading to adjoining cavities in the bone. If this occurs, not merely is hearing impaired but the prospects of healing are very slight. Sometimes the life of the person may be endangered in this way.

And now a few words about taste and smell. The upper and inner surface of each nostril is the external organ for smell. From each nostril a bundle of nerve-fibres passes up to the lower front part of the cerebrum and then by a roundabout route reaches the area for smell on the inner and under surface of the temporal lobe of the brain at each side.

Similarly, from the tongue and from much of the inner surface of the mouth, nerve-fibres carry messages to a surface on the brain just beside that for smell. The external organs for each sense—the nose and mouth—are close together, and their areas on the inner surface of each half of the base of the brain are also close together. The important thing to notice in the case of both taste and smell is that the nervous mechanisms really consist of three parts—the external organ, the ingoing nerve-fibres, and the areas on the brain surface.

When we speak, therefore, of a tea-taster or wine-taster having an educated sense of taste, we mean that the area for taste in his brain has been specially developed and educated. In the same way, the expert who can detect slight differences in the smell of different kinds of perfumes has had the area for smell in his brain specially developed and educated.

## CHAPTER XXXVIII

### THE BODY SENSES

Travellers in India tell us of fakirs in that country, who, in zeal for their religion, make a vow that they will hold the arm straight upward from the shoulder and not take it down for a year or two. At the end of this time, the muscles of the arm and shoulder have shrunken and become fixed; the fakir has lost all power of moving them

This never happens amongst us. People in this country who do not take exercise are never punished by their limbs becoming fixed. But it does always happen that children who take little exercise for a long time, gradually lose all liking for exercise and in fact dislike it. And, in many children, though not in all, lack of proper exercise leads to poor health, poor muscular development, and lack of brain growth.

One would suppose that poor health is punishment enough for neglect or refusal to take exercise, but sometimes further punishment is inflicted.

Just as the growth of the area on the brain for sight, for hearing, for taste, and for smell all depend upon their being exercised and trained; that is, upon their getting regular messages in great variety from the eye, ear, nose, and mouth; so the growth and health of another part of the brain called the "motor areas," depend upon their sending out regular messages to, and receiving regular messages from, the muscles of a child's body. Stagnation of muscles means poor development of part of the brain.

Look at the figure of one side of the brain, page 198. At the top and toward the front are printed the words, "areas which control movements of the leg, trunk, arm, face, movement of the eyes, and area for speech." As you have been already told, these parts of the brain together make up what are known as the "motor areas." Now, it is from these motor areas that messages, or commands, are sent out to the muscles of the body to make them move. When messages can not pass out from the motor areas, either because the areas themselves are diseased or because the nerve-fibres which carry the messages to the muscles are cut or diseased, then the muscles cannot produce any movement of the limbs or trunk.

When a person's backbone is broken, the nerve-fibres are injured where the backbone is broken, and the person cannot move the muscles of the lower part of his body and legs ; that is, the muscles are paralyzed. In addition to this, no messages of touch, pain, heat, or cold can be conveyed from the legs or feet to the brain, and the person is said "to have no feeling" in his legs ; that is, there is paralysis of all sensation. This is like what happens at the central station when all the wires are cut on a telegraph line.

But in health, messages are going in to the motor areas as well as passing out from them all the time. For example, if you shut your eyes and then place your arm and hand in any position, say above your head or to one side, you know exactly without looking at them where they are in relation to the rest of your body.

Suppose you raise your arm above your head, and point the first or index finger in any direction, you know where the finger is pointing just as well as if you were looking at it. Or, again, if you were lying blind-folded on your back, and a companion took hold of your hand and arm and made them point in any direction, you would know exactly where the arm was and where the hand was. You would know this from messages which travelled from the muscles or joints of your bent arm or fingers to the brain.

And what is true about messages from one hand or arm is true about messages coming from the muscles or joints of other parts of the body. Such messages tell us of all the possible positions of trunk and limbs, and are said to come from the "muscle sense." In other words, our muscles resemble the eyes and the ears in telling us about things that are going on in us and around us.

But, besides the muscle sense, there resides in the skin what is commonly called the sense of touch, though this sense rarely acts alone. Usually it acts along with the muscle sense. When we wish to know whether an object is rough or smooth we run our fingers over it; that is, we use our muscles as well as our finger-tips.

Again, if a person is blindfolded and put in a strange room, and asked how to find out all he can about its shape and contents, he will put out his arms in front of him and move forward until he touches one wall. Then he will stretch out his arms on each side, and move from side to side until he touches the two side walls. And so, by groping about in the dark as it were; that is, by using only the muscle sense and sense of touch, he comes to know a great deal about the room and what is in it.

We say then that the sense of touch is another of the body senses. Besides these two there are others which have to do with temperature and pressure. When a hot object or a cold object is made to touch the skin, we know it at once, and so we speak of a temperature sense. Then, too, when any light object, such as a feather, touches us, not merely do we know it by the sense of touch, but, if the hard tip of the feather be pressed against the skin at any point, we get another sensation, namely, that of pressure.

Lastly, there is the sense of pain. Every child knows that there pass in to the brain the most urgent messages whenever any part of the body is injured or becomes diseased. Notice, however, that no such messages are ever transmitted while we are in health and uninjured. Pain is always a sign of disease or injury and should never be neglected. It is Nature's warning to us that we are breaking some of her laws.

The body senses—muscle sense, touch, heat, cold, pressure—are no less important than the special senses of sight, hearing, taste, and smell. Their outer organs lie in the skin, in the joints, or in the muscles, and these organs are all connected by means of nerve-threads or fibres with special areas of the brain. These areas become specially educated or trained in those who follow any manual calling. For example, a watchmaker gets his muscle sense trained to skilful handling of delicate bits of machinery, and a silk sorter gets her sense of touch so well developed and educated that she recognizes at once slight differences in the quality of silk ; and so on in other callings. In fact, manual skill is always a training of the sense of touch, along with the muscle sense. As a rule, therefore, skilful mechanics can never be made of people who are weak-minded.

The training of the sensory and the motor areas of the brain in childhood is all important. If nerve messages from the muscles and skin do not reach the brain, certain parts of it will not grow properly. The opposite of this is also true. If the brain of a child is not normal, as in the case of an idiot, then normal nerve messages cannot be sent out to the muscles of the body. The sense of touch will therefore be defective, and this will be apparent in peculiar, jerky, or shuffling movements of the limbs, and in bluntness of feeling in different parts of the body.

## CHAPTER XXXIX

### ALCOHOL

Most people have noticed that a drunken man usually says foolish things and does foolish things. He thinks he can run farther, jump higher, work harder, write better, or count faster, with the aid of alcohol than without it. But this is all pure fancy. As to the use of his muscles, in either work or play, every one knows, who has ever seen a drunken man, that in place of being able to use his muscles properly, he can scarcely use them at all.

Scientific men, by a series of careful experiments, have learned beyond all question that alcohol—even a little of it—lessens a man's power of doing useful work. But, in addition to this scientific proof, there is the experience of men who employ large numbers of labourers. Such employers tell us that total abstainers do more work in a given time than an equal number of men who are moderate drinkers of alcohol, even though they may never get drunk.

Army officers tell us much the same thing about soldiers. Soldiers who are given no rations of whisky stand long marches and hard fighting better than soldiers who are supplied with alcohol. When we learn further that men who are being trained to take part in football, hockey, baseball, or rowing contests, are not allowed to drink alcohol or to smoke tobacco, we must conclude that the experience of their trainers has shown that these drugs do serious injury.

One of the most interesting tests of the effects of alcohol was that made upon skilled workmen by Dr. Aschaffenburg. Four experienced type-setters offered

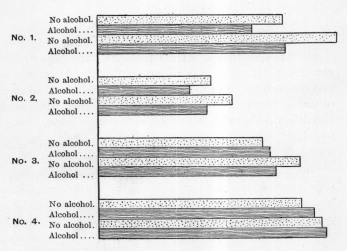

FIGURE 88.—Diagram showing type-setting results done by four men.

themselves for the experiment. Three of them were moderate drinkers, the fourth was known to drink hard now and again. After first determining the men's average ability, by counting the actual number of letters which each man set in four periods of fifteen minutes each per day, they were directed to work on four successive days for periods of fifteen minutes each, as in the preliminary tests.   On the second and fourth days each man was to take three tablespoonfuls of alcohol, but none on the first and third

The first man set up 2,339 letters on the first day without alcohol, but on the second day, with alcohol, only 2,212.   All four men thought they were doing more work with the alcohol than without it.   The fourth man was the regular drinker.   The results as to quantity of work done in the given time are shown in the diagram on page 215.

Those who drink wine or alcohol in small or moderate quantities deny that it harms them at all.   Many such people say that it does them good.   But even these people admit that they feel quite well without using any spirits, and that a cup of tea or coffee instead would probably do them as much or even more good.

If these people were familiar with the experiments which Professor McDougall carried on recently regarding the effects of alcohol and tea on mental fatigue, they would probably admit that tea is a real stimulant, whereas alcohol is not.   Alcohol, in fact, produces mental fatigue almost from the moment it is taken.

McDougall's experiments consisted in recording the number of errors which a healthy person made (1) without taking any drugs, (2) after taking from two to six tablespoonfuls of alcohol, and (3) after taking a cup or two of tea.   Here are two different records:

NUMBER OF ERRORS

|                    | No Drugs | Alcohol | Tea |
|--------------------|----------|---------|-----|
| First Record...........  | 379      | 583     | 273 |
| Second Record.........  | 298      | 351     | 291 |

The benefit of tea in diminishing errors, and the bad effects of alcohol in increasing them, is here clearly shown.

A few years ago Professor Kræpelin of Heidelberg carried out a great many experiments with alcohol, the results of which go to show that, even in small doses, amounting to not more than a tablespoonful, alcohol lessens a man's power of doing mental work. For example, the speed and accuracy with which his students, could add, subtract, multiply, and divide numbers in arithmetic were tested. They imagined that they could make arithmetical calculations more quickly with alcohol than without it, but the facts were exactly the reverse.

In one case a student was directed to add columns of figures for half-an-hour a day for six days. This was done in order to determine the average speed and accuracy with which he could work.

On the seventh day he began taking about two table-spoonfuls of alcohol, and continued this for thirteen days. His ability to add, in place of being maintained as it was on the sixth day, was at once decreased, and continued to decrease. On the nineteenth day the use of alcohol was stopped, when a gain in speed and accuracy at once became apparent.

Memory was tested by setting students to memorize columns of figures. It was found that 100 figures could be remembered correctly after being repeated 40 times. But when alcohol was given it was found that only 60 figures could be remembered after being repeated 60 times.

Sweden was the first country to test the effects of alcohol upon quick and accurate rifle shooting. A number of officers and soldiers, all good shots, were directed to shoot at a target 200 yards distant. The tests were made several times a day, and on different days. When alcohol in doses of three tablespoonfuls was given, 30 per cent fewer hits were made, although the men all thought they were shooting faster and more accurately with alcohol than without it.

Bad as are the effects of alcohol upon the drunkard himself, the effects upon his children are very much worse. They are often left without food, clothing, and education ; but these are small ills compared with the supreme one which a drunkard sometimes brings upon his innocent offspring, namely, insanity.

The almost unvarying testimony of medical superintendents of lunatic asylums is that the drunkenness of fathers or mothers often entails upon children enfeebled brain and nerves, with the result that, when the strain and stress of adult life come upon them, brain and mind break down and they become inmates of lunatic asylums.

Dr. C. K. Clarke, Medical Superintendent of the Toronto Hospital for the Insane and Dean of the Faculty of Medicine in the University of Toronto, has stated, in one of his official reports, that in his opinion a large number of the patients in all lunatic asylums in

Canada either are the offspring of alcoholic parents or have become insane through drink

In support of Dr. Clarke's views, it may be stated that of the 10,445 males and 10,852 females who were admitted into the insane asylums of England and Wales in 1906, about 22 per cent. of the male cases, and 9 per cent. of the female ones were caused by alcohol. These figures do not include those cases in which the insanity or mental breakdown was due to drunkenness in the parents. If such cases were taken into account, it would be found that fully 20 per cent. of all the cases of insanity in Britain are caused by alcohol

That alcohol increases crime has long been known. In Sweden, between 1887 and 1897, no fewer than 17,374 persons were sentenced for crimes of various kinds. Of this number of crimes, about 71 per cent. were traceable to drink. In Massachusetts, U.S., from August, 1894, to August, 1895, 8,440 persons were sentenced for somewhat serious crimes, and of these 43 per cent. were committed while the criminal was under the influence of liquor.

Again, it is quite safe to say that the continued use of alcohol, even in moderate quantities, shortens life. No one knows this better than the chief physician of a life insurance company. The business of such a man is to give advice to the company about men whom it is safe to insure and about men whom it is not safe to insure. A man who wishes to get his life insured must first answer a number of questions about himself, his father and mother, grandfather and grandmother, and brothers and sisters, if he has any. Then a doctor examines the man's heart, kidneys, lungs, and respiration. All the facts which the man himself gives and all those which the doctor finds out about the man's health, are written down and sent to the chief physician of the insurance company. Whether the company will insure the man's life or not will depend upon the advice of the chief physician. If the man uses alcohol even in moderate quantities, some companies will not take the risk ; or, if they do, they charge a higher rate, because they say that such a man will not likely live so long as a man who does not take alcohol at all.

### EXPECTATION OF LIFE, *by Baër.*

| Age | | Abstainers are likely to live | | Alcohol users are likely to live |
|---|---|---|---|---|
| At 25 | .. | 30.08 years | .. | 26.23 years |
| 35 | .. | 25.92 " | .. | 20.01 " |
| 45 | .. | 19.92 " | .. | 15.19 " |
| 55 | .. | 14.45 " | .. | 11.15 " |
| 65 | .. | 9.62 " | .. | 8.04 " |

Such a table as this has been compiled from the reports of physicians who have attended the sick during their last illness. A physician soon comes to find out whether his patients are users of alcohol or not. He is compelled by law to report the cause of every death to a government official. In this way it has become known that steady drinkers, even though they may never have been drunk in their lives, are liable to suffer from certain diseases. For example, it has been observed that diseases of the heart, blood-vessels, stomach, kidneys, and liver are more common among such people than they are among total abstainers ; and it has been noticed also that the use of alcohol makes some diseases, such as indigestion and gout, much worse than they would otherwise be.

The conclusion from all this is obvious : alcohol is a very dangerous drug ; its continued use soon passes into a habit which enslaves and destroys both mind and body ; and therefore the only safe rule to follow regarding it is to avoid its use altogether.

## CHAPTER XL

### NARCOTICS : OPIUM, TOBACCO, COCAINE

A narcotic is a substance which either puts one asleep or at least benumbs the nervous system and prevents its healthy action. Alcohol, ether, chloroform, bromide of potash, chloral hydrate, cocaine, opium and an extract from it called morphia, are narcotics. Used in small quantities they seem to excite the nerves and stir up the machinery of the body just as tea and coffee do ; but they are not really stimulants. When taken in larger quantities, they dull the nerves and finally put a man into a deep sleep such as we often see in the drunkard. You will, of course, understand that they do not act upon all of us to the same extent when taken in equally large or small doses.

Ether and chloroform are liquids which rapidly turn into an invisible vapour. Taken into the body through the lungs along with the air which we breathe they produce the profound sleep into which people are thrown before they undergo a serious surgical operation.

Ether, alcohol, and chloroform resemble one another in another respect; they make those who take them believe that they are stronger, quicker, and more able to do things with the aid of the drug than without it. How groundless this belief is in the case of alcohol has already been shewn.

These three drugs also reduce the body temperature below the point at which it stands in good health. For this reason a person who has undergone any surgical operation under ether or chloroform is afterwards kept in bed for a time with hot-water bottles about his body.

Alcohol also in large doses produces the deep sleep of the drunkard. So too, bromide of potash, opium, and some substances which are made from coal tar, possess this same numbing and deadening effect. The nicotine of tobacco in the minute doses in which it gets into the body in smoking, rarely does more than soothe or dull nervous sensibility; nevertheless it also belongs to the class of narcotics.

Lastly, all the drugs of this class create a strong and often uncontrollable desire to take more of them, until at last the drug habit is developed, and then health speedily becomes ruined and life prospects blighted.

In this chapter we shall consider briefly the effects of only three of the narcotics, opium, cocaine, and tobacco. Opium and its extract, morphine, are among the most useful of drugs, for they deaden the nerves and relieve great pain when perhaps nothing else will. But the drug should be used with great caution, and only under the advice of a physician. It should never be used as a remedy for sleeplessness. An uncontrollable craving for it comes on much sooner than for alcohol. It is, therefore, just so much the more dangerous.

Chloral and cocaine resemble opium somewhat in their effects. Chloral is sometimes used to make people sleep, and cocaine is often forced into the flesh to deaden pain, when the surgeon is about to perform some slight but painful operation.

Perhaps the greatest danger of acquiring the cocaine habit comes from using the drug in the form of an ointment for rubbing into the nostrils, when a person is suffering from nasal catarrh, a disease which usually comes on as the result of a succession of colds in the nose. When this disease has lasted for a long time, it becomes very trying to the health. A man is thus greatly tempted to use such an ointment, and almost before he knows of the danger, he has acquired the cocaine habit. Whether rubbed into the nose or taken in some kind of drink, the habit, once it is formed, is very difficult to break off.

No doubt some medical men have been much too careless in the past, in advising people to take alcohol, opium, chloral, and other narcotics. The use of these medicines under the direction of a wise physician for a very short time is right; but the danger of becoming a slave to their use is so great, that both physician and patient should always be on their guard. Many of the diseases for which these drugs are given, if curable at all, can be cured only by a surgical operation or by practising a healthful mode of living.

When we come to consider tobacco, we have to do with a drug that, in some respects, is unlike the others that have been mentioned. In the first place, its use does not produce the same evil effects upon mind and morals ; and, though men do become slaves to it, and though its use in some cases impairs digestion, injures the throat, upsets the regular beat of the heart, and weakens the nervous system, yet in many other cases, no evil consequences appear to follow from using it.

While it cannot be proved that the practice of smoking tobacco stunts the growth of boys, so far as mere size is concerned, we do know that its effects fall pretty heavily upon their brain and spinal cord. It prevents the nerves from growing as strong as they should, and this means in the end a more delicate body. The effects upon the nerves may easily be noticed in the trembling of the hand in boys who smoke much, especially if they inhale the smoke; that is, pass it down into the throat. When smoking is carried on in this latter way, more of the poison of the tobacco, "nicotine," is passed into the body, and it produces a more marked effect upon the nerves. Employers of labour have frequently noticed that young men who smoke many cigarettes are forgetful and are less reliable in their work than non-smokers.

The question of whether you will use tobacco or not is a very serious one. Before you decide to use it, you should try to think of its effects upon others as well as upon yourselves. Its bad effects upon other people in the same house are often overlooked. Tobacco smoke in houses is hurtful to young children, and a great annoyance to those who do not smoke. If several men are smoking in a small room, the air soon becomes quite unfit for anyone to breathe. Much less is it fit for a delicate person or a child to live in. So that, if any of you should come to be bent on smoking, knowing all the time the risk to your own health, you ought at least to pay some attention, while indulging the habit, to the health and feelings of others. No person has a right to spoil the air which others have to breathe.

Does tobacco smoking hurt a grown-up man? Yes; it does in some cases, unless the man is very robust. It is impossible to prove that smoking hurts a strong healthy man who is living a regular outdoor life. But, in the case of men who have not been born strong, who live an indoor life, and who do not take much exercise, there can be no reasonable doubt that smoking tends in time to undermine the health. Many men have found this out for themselves. Some, when upwards of forty years of age, have succeeded, by great effort, in giving up the habit. How much better, if they had never learned it!

## CHAPTER XLI

### FAMILY STOCK

Turn to the frontispiece and study for a little the copy of that celebrated painting called "Thoroughbred." There are four figures in the picture, a young girl, a race-horse, and two dogs. Which is the thoroughbred— the girl, the horse, or the dogs? Or are they all thoroughbred? What is meant by thoroughbred? Does it not mean that all four are descended through the best blood from a long line of ancestors?

You know how particular many farmers are about the breed of their cattle, horses, and dogs. They are proud of their Jersey cows, their Percheron horses, or their

Collie dogs, and they take the greatest pains to keep the race as purely bred as possible. And, in somewhat the same way, there are many parents to-day who are most anxious that their sons and daughters should make proper marriages. With them it is not a question of marrying into a wealthy family; but, it is a question of soundness of body, purity of life, and purity of morals.

The large mass of the population of America belong to a good sound stock; but there is also in every district a certain number of families who are weaklings or are diseased in body and impure and depraved in mind and life.

In order to make the difference between two such families as clear as possible, I propose to lay before you a very brief history of a bad family—the Juke, and an equally brief history of a good family—the Edwards, the latter having amongst its members the celebrated divine and philosopher, Jonathan Edwards.

It is to the late Mr. Richard Dugdale that we are indebted for the history of the notorious Juke family. His special purpose in studying its members was to find out, if possible, whether or not criminal parents usually have criminal children, and whether such children, on becoming men and women and marrying, have criminal children. In other words, he wished to know whether crime and pauperism run in families from father to son throughout a number of generations.

After years of patient toil in gathering the facts about these people and their immediate relatives, Mr. Dugdale came to realize that they had all sprung from a long line of ancestors reaching back to the early days of the settlement of the state. The forefather of the family on the father's side was born between the years 1720 and 1740, and was called Max. This Max was descended from early Dutch settlers and lived much as our backwoodsmen do to-day in remote settlements. In old age, he became blind from a disease which was passed on to his children and grandchildren. He had a large family. Two of his five sons married two out of six sisters who were the female ancestors of the Juke family.

The Juke sisters were born between the years 1740 and 1760. One of the six known as Ada Juke, though this was not her real name, left one son, who became the father of a line of descendants, many of whom were criminals through five generations. For this reason she has long been known to the police as " Margaret, the mother of criminals." The fifth sister was the mother of a line of descendants most of whom, in place of being criminals as in the case of Ada's children, were paupers ; that is, they were never able to earn enough money to keep themselves in food, shelter, and clothing.

It is impossible for me to state the particulars about the drunkenness, vagrancy, pauperism, licentiousness, disease, and crime of the Juke family ; but, when you become men and women you may be interested in reading them for yourselves.

The number of descendants whose records have been traced reaches 540 persons—all related by blood to the Jukes. The number related to them by marriage is 169 or 709 persons in all, alive and dead. But it is quite certain that there are about 500 others who are related to the Jukes, but whose relationship it has not been possible to trace on account of their migrations from place to place.

After drawing up a statement of the loss in labour and wages, and the cost of supporting the family at the public expense, Mr. Dugdale says :—" Over a million and a quarter dollars of loss in 75 years caused by a single family 1,200 strong, without reckoning the cash paid for whisky, or taking into account the entailment of pauperism and crime on the survivors in succeeding generations, and the incurable disease, idiocy, and insanity growing out of this debauchery and reaching further than we can calculate. It is getting to be time to ask, do our courts, our laws, our almshouses and our jails deal with the question presented ?"

It is scarcely possible to conceive of a greater contrast between two families than that between the Jukes and the Edwards. In one group there was scarcely a strain of industry scholarship, or virtue. They were ignorant, profane, licentious, idle paupers and criminals. In the other group, you find ability, character, high purpose in life, and magnificent achievement. Max and Jonathan Edwards were both country lads. Both lived on the frontier, and were, therefore, far removed from the opportunity of getting either a High School or a College education. Looking back from this distance of time, one would naturally think that each man had an equal chance for success in life. But he had not. Their own lives and that of their children show most clearly how the blessing of a good heredity, or the curse of a bad one, handicaps a family stock for generations. Max, as we have seen, gave 1,200 descendants to the world, noted chiefly for their licentiousness, pauperism and crime ; while Edwards has become the ancestor of some 1,400 men and women, distinguished all over the United States and Canada for their virtue, honesty, earnestness, nobility, and high achievements. Not one of Max's 1,200 descendants ever secured even a High School education. They all lacked the inherited capacity or training without which all high achievement is impossible. Only 20 of the Jukes ever learned a trade, and then only in the state prison.

On the other hand, the Edwards family inherited great capacity for training. No fewer than 285 of the descendants were college graduates. Thirteen of these became college presidents. Sixty-five are college professors, many are principals of High schools and academies, and many others are prominent in business and professional life.

When within a dozen years from now you begin to think of selecting a life partner, I beg of you to consider whether it will be best for you to marry into a Juke family or into a Jonathan Edwards one.

If you have followed the teachings of this book thus far, it must be clear to you now that our lives from birth until old age are shaped largely by two great influences : (1) by what we inherit from parents, grandparents, or other ancestral relatives, and (2) by our environment, that is, by our surroundings.

Our lives are being moulded every day we live by our environment—by the air and light about us, the food we eat, the liquids we drink, the clothing we wear, the houses we live in, the earth we walk on or dig in, the water we bathe in, the people we associate with in schools and churches, the sights we see at home or when we travel.

All of these affect us more or less throughout life. Environment and heredity—these are the two factors that largely mould human life.

As illustrating how potent these factors are I need only remind you of the high death-rate among infants in Ontario, in 1907. Out of 53,584 babies born in that year, no fewer than 8,041 died before they were one year old. When we look into the causes of death, we find that about 1,700 were dead at birth, and that about 1,500 other deaths are reported as due to congenital debility; in other words, 3,200 infants died because of a defective heredity. We may assume that about 800 more must have died from the same cause, though this is not clearly stated in the reports to the government.

Deducting the number who thus died because of their defective heredity from the total of 8,041, would leave about 4,000 who died because of the unfavourable environment into which they were born. Looking into the cause of the death of these 4,000, we find that about 1,400 are reported as dying of diarrhœa, indigestion, or inflammation of the intestines; about 1,200 more as dying of diseases of the air-passages like pneumonia and bronchitis; while hundreds of others are reported as dying from causes which every physician knows to be preventable. It is safe to say that the lives of 2,000 babies could be saved annually, if parents were only sufficiently intelligent or sufficiently trained to care properly for their offspring.

If parents take good care of their children, giving them plenty of good food, that is, milk, eggs, fruits, vegetables, bread, butter, soups, and easily digested meats; sending them to play much and often in the sunshine and fresh air; providing them with clean warm clothing in winter and light cool clothing in summer; and seeing that they get enough sleep; many more of them than at present are likely to grow up with sound minds and sound bodies.

Almost the whole of this book is devoted to an attempt to show how our environment influences our health, happiness, and success in life. Little has been said about heredity; but the heredity of the Juke family has been dealt with for the purpose of placing you on your guard against selecting for a life partner a member of a tainted family.

We all come into the world stamped with a certain quality of blood, brawn, and brain, and quite unable to make geniuses out of ourselves if we have been born weaklings in mind. A Juke cannot change himself into a Jonathan Edwards. But a man may hope by the exercise of his will and reason to dominate even an unfavourable environment and heredity, and command a considerable measure of success in life.

## CHAPTER XLII

### EMERGENCIES

In case of an accident, every boy and girl should know what to do before the doctor comes. A boy who is quick to think and quick to act may often be of great service to one who is bleeding profusely, or who has taken poison, or who is unconscious and almost dead from being under water.

## DROWNING

When taken from the water, a person should first be turned face downward and held up by the middle with his head low, in order to allow the water to run out of his mouth and lungs. Loosen the collar quickly, but do not take time to remove the clothing. If respiration has ceased, artificial respiration must be commenced at once ; every instant of delay is serious. To do this, the patient should be placed upon his back with a block of wood or a folded coat under his back. Then one person should raise the patient's arms horizontally above his head and lower them again to his sides. As the patient's arms reach his sides, another person should press upon his stomach and the edge of his chest, so as to diminish the size of the chest and aid in the expulsion of air. These movements should be continued at the rate of about seventeen per minute. Efforts at resuscitation should be kept up for an hour or even longer. During this time others may apply warmth to the body by means of hot flannels, hot water bottles, etc.

Figures 89, 90 and 91 show how artificial respiration can be carried on by one person. Pupils should practise it on one another.

## ANOTHER METHOD

Two objections have often been urged against keeping the patient lying upon his back while carrying on artificial respiration. The first is that the tongue may slip backward and close the entrance to the windpipe. The second objection is that the water, mucus, and froth in the windpipe prevent the free entrance of the air.

FIGURE 89

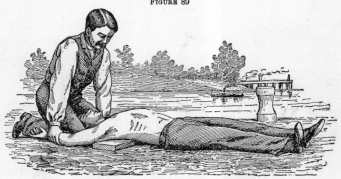

FIGURE 90.

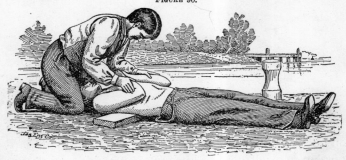

FIGURE 91.

FIGURES 89, 90 and 91.—How artificial respiration is carried on by one person.

Professor Schäfer, of Edinburgh University, therefore, advises that the patient be placed "face downwards on the ground with a folded coat under the lower part of the chest."

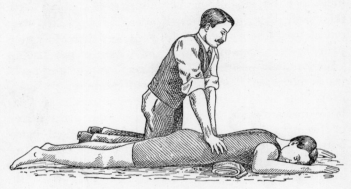

FIGURE 92.

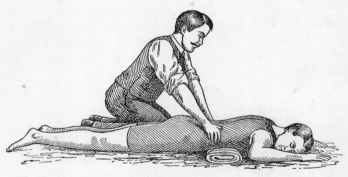

FIGURE 93.

" To effect artificial respiration," he says, "put yourself on one side of the patient's body or astride of it, supporting yourself on one knee upon one side, and on one foot on the other side. Place your hands flat over the lower part of the back (on the lowest ribs), one on each side, and gradually throw the weight of your body forward on to them so as to produce firm pressure—which must not be violent—upon the patient's chest. By this means air (and water if there is any) is driven out of the patient's lungs. Immediately thereafter raise your body so as to remove the pressure, but having your hands in position. Repeat this forward and backward movement (pressure and relaxation of pressure) every four or five seconds. In other words, sway your body forwards and backwards upon your arms fifteen or twenty times a minute without any marked pause between the movements. This course must be pursued for at least half an hour, or until the natural respirations are resumed.

"Whilst one person is carrying out artificial respiration in this way, others may, if there be opportunity, busy themselves with applying hot flannels to the body and limbs, and hot bottles to the feet." After natural respiration has begun, massage should be applied to the limbs.

## BLEEDING, OR HEMORRHAGE

If a large artery or vein in a limb is cut a physician should be summoned at once. The rapid flow of blood from a large vessel prevents clotting. Under these circumstances, the limb should at once be grasped firmly with the hands and pressure applied above the wound (nearer to the heart) if it is an artery, and below the wound (nearer the hand or foot) if it is a vein. While pressure is being thus maintained upon the artery or the vein, a strong handkerchief or cord should be tied loosely round the limb and a stick run below the handkerchief and twisted so as to bring great pressure to bear upon the bleeding vessels. This will stop the most profuse bleeding in any limb.

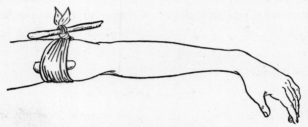

FIGURE 94.—Tourniquet or bandage twisted tight with a stick.

If, however, no large blood-vessel has been cut, it is important to know what to do in order to help the blood to clot. Perhaps the best thing is to apply hot water to the injured part. The water should be as hot as can be borne. The heat makes the small vessels shrink in diameter, and this, along with the clot which forms, soon stops the bleeding. If the bleeding cannot be stopped in this way, place a firm pad of clean cotton upon the wound and then tie a bandage tightly around it.

If the wound has been made with a dirty knife, tin can, rusty nail, or glass, it should be thoroughly washed before bandaging with hot water to which has been added some antiseptic such as listerine or euthymol.

## FAINTING

Fainting is usually caused by the blood-flow to the brain being cut off or very much reduced. Consequently the first thing to be done in order to restore conscious-ness is to promote the return of the blood to the brain. This is usually done by lowering the head and raising the legs and feet. In addition, the clothing should be loosened around the neck and chest, fresh air admitted to the room, and a touch of cold water applied to the face.

Strong ammonia or smelling salts should not be held to the nose of a person who is in a faint. It is very irritating and as a rule does no good.

## DISLOCATION

If bones are forced out of their natural position in a joint, they are said to be "dislocated." When bones are thus dislocated some of the ligaments may be broken and the bones must be put back again along the same course by which they came out. In simple disloca-tions of the fingers or wrists, the bones can generally be returned to their natural position by pulling on the joint and pressing the bones back into their place.

A sprain is a tear or strain of the ligaments of a joint, but without dislocation of the bones. A tear is much more serious than a strain. In either case, the joint should be bathed thoroughly in water as hot as can be borne for ten or fifteen minutes. This should be accompanied with brisk rubbing of the joint. Then the joint should be rested for some time according to the extent of the injury.

## FRACTURES

In all fractures of bone, the chief thing to do before a surgeon can be secured is to keep the limb or broken part

at rest.    If the patient has to be moved some distance to
his home or to a hospital, he should be
carried upon a door, shutter, or board.
Before doing this, however, the limb
should be tied to a thin piece of straight
wood, so that it cannot move. Or
an umbrella or walking stick may be
used, or the two legs, in case of one
being broken, may be tied together.
Handkerchiefs make good temporary
bandages. When necessary, clothes
should be removed by opening them
along the seams

FIGURE 95. — Tempo-
rary splint and band-
age on a broken leg.
Enough bandages
should be applied to
prevent movement
of the limb.

## SUNSTROKE

The main symptom of sunstroke, or
heatstroke, as it is sometimes called, is
the high temperature. A clinical or
other small thermometer placed in the
mouth shows a temperature varying
between 105° F. and 112° F. Consequently, the first thing to do is to place
the patient in a cold bath ; ice, if con-
venient, being applied to the head and
body.    The cold water treatment must be continued until
the temperature falls to the normal.

## BURNS AND SCALDS

When a girl's clothes are on fire she should never
run about. This only fans the flame. She should be
forced to lie down, so that the flames may not rise
round her head and neck, where they do most injury.
If a bucket of water is at hand it should be dashed

over her. If not, woollen clothes, such as a blanket, rug, shawl, or overcoat should be wrapped round her body to extinguish the flames.

The emergent treatment of scalds is much the same as that for burns. Clothing should be removed by cutting, or opening along the seams. A warm bath of 100° F. or hot-water bottles around the body, a stimulant of hot coffee, and perhaps a mustard plaster over the heart, will all contribute to overcome the great prostration that always follows a severe burn or scald. The burned or scalded parts should be covered with strictly clean, soft linen cloths covered with boric acid solution, or boric acid ointment, and over these should be placed a wrapping of raw cotton or oiled silk, so as to exclude as far as possible all contact with the air.

## POISONS

The Imperial dictionary defines a poison as " any agent capable of producing a morbid, noxious, or deadly effect upon the animal economy when introduced either by cutaneous absorption, respiration, or the digestive canal." This definition will include a large number of substances not usually considered poisonous; but the fact is that it is difficult to define a poison. The effect of many substances upon the human body depends upon the quantity, or dose, that has been taken.

When common household poisons, such as paris green, fly poisons, corrosive sublimate (which is often used as a disinfectant), paregoric, soothing syrup, ends of matches, are taken by accident, the first thing to do is to send for a physician. While awaiting his arrival, however, it is generally advisable to induce vomiting. This may be done by giving a teaspoonful of mustard in a glass of warm water. Repeat the dose in about ten minutes if the first produces no effect.

After the emetic, the following antidotes may be given to counteract the effects of any of the poison which may remain in the body :—

1. For any kind of lead poisoning (sugar of lead, or white lead), give a large dose of Epsom salts or Glauber's salts.

2. For corrosive sublimate, solution of bluestone, or verdigris, give the whites of several eggs, or large quantities of flour and water.

3. For opium poisoning (paregoric, soothing syrup, laudanum), keep the patient walking about and give frequent drinks of strong coffee.

4. For strychnia poisoning, administer ether or chloroform to relieve the muscular spasms. If the respiration stops, keep up artificial respiration.

5. In arsenic poisoning (paris green or fly poisons), mix tincture of iron with baking soda, and give the patient every minute or two a teaspoonful of the brownish powder that forms.

6. For poisoning with matches, give the whites of several eggs, or a dessertspoonful of powdered charcoal.

For acid poisons, such as nitric, sulphuric, carbolic, or muriatic acid, give at once, without producing vomiting, three or four spoonfuls of baking soda, or a glass or two of lime-water.

## CONVULSIONS

When in convulsions, or fits, a person should be placed where he will not strike his arms or legs against anything hard. Often the patient foams at his mouth and grinds his teeth. To prevent him from biting his tongue, a spoon or lead-pencil with a handkerchief wound round it should be inserted between his teeth.

## Frost-bites

The part which has become frost-bitten should be covered with a muffler or gently rubbed with fur. It should not be bathed with warm water. Nor should the patient be sent into a warm room. Gentle rubbing with snow, or bathing the part in ice-cold water are also suitable remedies.

## Electric Shock

If the body is in contact with a "live wire," it should be removed from the wire by using a dry stick, or a dry piece of clothing. Do not use your bare hands to move the body, or you may be injured yourself. If breathing has ceased, perform artificial respiration at once and keep it up for at least half an hour.

# PRONUNCIATION OF DIFFICULT WORDS

Adenoid (ad'en-oid).
Antidote (an'ti-dōt).
Antiseptic (an-ti-sep'tik).
Argon (är'gon).
Arsenic (är'sen-ik).
Auricle (a̤'ri-kl).
Anopheles (a-nof'e-lēz).
Aqueous (ak'wē-us).

Bacillus (ba-sil'lus).
Bacterium (bak-tē'ri-um).
Bichloride (bi-klō'rīd).
Bronchitis (brong-kī'tis).
Bromide (brō'mīd or brō'mid).
Bubonic (bū-bon'ik).

Capillaries (kap'il-la-ries or
  ka-pil'la-ries).
Carbohydrate (kär'bō-hī-drāt).
Carbolic (kär-bol'ik).
Cementum (sē-men'tum).
Catarrh (ka-tär').
Chloral (klō'ral).
Chronic (kron'ik).
Cholera (kol'ér-a).
Chloride (klō'rīd).
Choroid (kor'oid).
Constipation (kon-sti-pā'shon).
Corrosive (ko-rōs'iv).
Corpuscles (kor'pus-ls).
Cerebrum (sér'ē-brum).
Cerebellum (sér-ē-bel'lum).
Cocaine (kō'ka-in).
Cornea (kor'nē-a).
Ciliary (sil'i-a-ri).

Clinical (klin'ik-al).
Congenital (kon-jen'it-al).
Chloroform (klō'rō-form).

Dentine, dentin (den'tin).
Dioxide (dī-oks'īd).
Diarrhœa (dī-a-rē'a).
Digitalis (di-jit-ā'lis).
Diphtheria (dif-thē'ri-a).
Duodenum (dū-ō-dē'num).
Dyspepsia (dis-pep'si-a).

Emetic (ē-met'ik).
Enteric (en-ter'ik).
Epiglottis (e-pi-glot'is).
Erysipelas (e-ri-sip'e-las).
Eustachian (u-stā'ki-an).
Ether (ē'thér).
Euthymol (ū-thī'-mol).
Excretory (eks'krē-to-ri).

Follicle (fol'li-kl).
Formaldehyde (fôrm-al'dē-hīd).

Gangrene (gang'grēn).
Germicide (jér'-mi-sīd).
Glycogen (glī'ko-jen).
Glauber (gla̤'bér).

Hemorrhage (hē'mor-āj).
Hippocrates (Hip-poc'ra-tes).
Hydrate (hī'drāt).

Influenza (in-flū-en'za).
Iris (ī-ris).

243

Jugular (jū′gū-lér).

Laboratory (lab′o-ra-to-ri).
Lactic (lak′tik).
Laudanum (lạd′a-num).
Lymph (limf).
Listerine (lis′ter-in).
Lagrippe (or la grippe)

Massage (mäs-äzh′).
Malaria (ma-lā′ri-a).
Microbe (mī′krōb).
Mitral (mī′tral).
Mucous (mū′kus).
Muriatic (mū-ri-at′ik).

Narcotic (när-kot′ik).
Nicotine (nik′ō-tin).
Nitrogen (nī′trō-jen).
Nitric (nī′trik).
Nutritive (nū′tri-tiv).

Opium (ō′pi-um).
Oxygen (oks′i-jen).

Pasteurize (pas-tér′īz).
Proteid (prō′tē-id).
Phthisis (thī′sis).

Pancreatic (pán-krē-at′ik).
Paralysis (pa-ral′i-sis).
Paregoric (par-e-gor′ik).
Plasma (plaz′ma).

Retina (ret′i-na).

Sanatorium (san-a-tō′ri-um).
Sclerotic (sklē-rot′ik).
Soldanella (sol-da-nel′la).
Sporozoa (spō-rō-zō′a).
Sputum (spū′tum).
Stegomeyia (ste-go-mīe′-ah).
Strychnia (strik′ni-a).
Sulphuric (sul-fū′rik).
Sublimate (sub′li-māt).

Tartar (tär′tar).
Tricuspid (trī-kusp′id).
Tubercle (tū′bér-kl).
Tuberculosis (tū-bér′kū-lō″sis).
Typhoid (tī′foid).

Uvula (ū′vū-la).

Ventricle (ven′tri-kl).
Verdigris (vér′di-gris).
Vitreous (vit′rē-us).

# INDEX

## A.

Air, dust in, 10.
" effects of bad, 13.
" fresh, 7.
" movements of, 18.
" space in houses, 184.
" stuffy, 11, 12.
Alcohol, 99, 120, 121, 122, 125, 214, 216, 217, 219, 221.
Antidotes, 240.
Area for hearing, 198, 207.
" " sight, 201, 205.
" " smell, 198, 209.
" " taste, 198, 209.
Argon, 9
Artificial respiration, 232, 235.
Ashes from the body, 24.

## B.

Bacteria, 27, 31, 32, 33, 35, 36.
" and water, 38, 39.
" lactic acid, 156.
" seasonal, 40.
" useful, 38.
Barn-yard, 156.
Baths, 68.
Bedrooms, 185, 187.
Bleeding, or hemorrhage, 235.
Blood, 103, 104.
Body, burning of, 22.
Body heat, 123, 124, 137.
Body senses, 210, 212.
Bolting food, 75.
Brain and bulb, 195, 197, 200.
Burning candle in jar, 23.
Burns and scalds, 238.

## C.

Capillaries, 104.
Carbon dioxide, 8.
Chicken-pox, 40.
Circulation of blood, 108, 110.
" rate of, 109.
" scheme, 105.
Cleanliness, 52, 57.
Clothing, 136, 138, 140
Cocaine, 223.
Coffee, 97.
Colds, 72, 208.
Cold storage, 37.
Composition of air, 7.
" " foods, 95.
Constipation, 82.
Consumption, 170, 174, 176, 178, 180.
Contagion, 50, 51.
Convulsions, 240.
Cows, clean, 157, 159, 169.

## D.

Deaths from consumption, 175,176.
Desks, 129, 130.
Diarrhœa, 82.
Diet and exercise, 90, 92.
" " growth, 93.
Digestion, 78, 79.
Diphtheria, 40, 168.
Disease and street cars, 45.
" in houses, 182.
Disinfectant, 55.
Dislocation, 237.
Distillation, 120.
Drowning, 232, 234.